/10/ LINDA LOVE JIMMY

*Jimmy McGhee*

# *Pollock:*

# Agricultural Implement Makers 1867-2017

# *Pollock:*
# Agricultural Implement Makers 1867-2017

Jimmy McGhee

CARN PUBLISHING

© Jimmy McGhee, 2017.
First Published in Great Britain, 2017.


ISBN – 978 1 911043 04 1



Published by Carn Publishing,
Lochnoran House,
Auchinleck, Ayrshire, KA18 3JW.



Printed by Bell & Bain Ltd,
Glasgow, G46 7UQ.

# Contents

# List of Illustrations

## Foreword

It is a significant achievement for a company to reach its one hundred and fiftieth anniversary. It is an even greater achievement if that company is a Scottish agricultural implement and machine maker: few of them have reached that milestone. Pollock Farm Equipment Ltd is one such company. Since its founding by Andrew Pollock in 1867, as Andrew Pollock (Mauchline) Ltd, the company has been at the forefront of agricultural innovation, developing award-winning implements and machines to the highest standard of workmanship and materials. Pollock has been a by-word for innovation, quality and practicability, as it is today.

Back in the 1870s, Andrew Pollock focused his attention on making implements and machines for the local farming community in Ayrshire, and principally around the Mauchline district. It wasn't long until he had his eyes on a wider market. In 1871, he started to advertise his products in the *North British Agriculturist*, the leading farming paper of the day. It had a readership throughout Scotland and a circulation that extended well-beyond it, throughout the world. In 1875 Andrew exhibited at his first Highland Show, enabling him to bring his products to the attention of farmers throughout Scotland and beyond. He attended the show in all of its show districts, and became a regular exhibitor, as the company is today. He also attended local shows throughout Scotland, as well as the all-important Smithfield Show in London, where only a handful of Scottish manufacturers exhibited. That alone distinguished the company from the many other smaller manufacturers throughout the country. All were important in bringing Andrew's manufactures to a wider market and developing a network that has continued to this day, enabling the company to become a global one, as it remains.

In its 150 years, the company has witnessed huge changes in Scottish agriculture, in the way that the land is managed and used, farming and livestock practices and the implements and machinery on the farm. It has adapted to these changes, developing new machines and implements. In the 1870s its products included potato diggers, potato dressers, turnip slicers, curd mills and sack barrows. By the 1890s they included potato diggers, reaping and mowing machines, hay and straw presses, hay collectors, rick lifters, curd mills and cheese presses. Carts were to follow in the first decade of the twentieth century, as was the harvest tedder in 1910. These were to lay the basis for the company's products for decades; others have been added to that illustrious catalogue.

As an agricultural historian, I am delighted to be able to celebrate Pollock Farm Equipment's significant achievement. I hope that you will enjoy Jimmy McGhee's history of the company.

Dr Heather Holmes
Scottish Agricultural Implement Makers

# Introduction

The history of Pollock's agricultural implement makers is one that deserves to be recorded. The company was founded in 1867 in Mauchline, when Andrew Pollock was able to develop the Cowgatehead Smiddy into something more than just the normal agricultural smithy, showing horses and doing basic metalwork repairs. His acumen and skill in developing new and better tools and machinery meant that he was destined for greater things.

The company has developed over the years, enabling it to survive fifteen decades of change in agriculture, from when horsepower was literal, to modern times, when many machines are controlled by computer, something that even Andrew Pollock would never be able to anticipate. That it did develop, has meant that it has outlasted many of its near competitors.

I have had a personal connection with the last fifty years of the business, from being an apprentice in 1967 to owning the business today. The firm has meant very much to me, and I have been honoured to be able to develop the business into its present format. Hopefully, the name Pollock will still be well-known in agricultural circles in another fifty years' time, and new developments will still be being made in Ayrshire.

I would like to thank everyone who has assisted in making this book possible. Firstly, to Roseanne Savage for typing the manuscript and managing to decipher my handwriting. Secondly, to the many folk who supplied photographs old and new for this book, or else provided implements. To the Royal Highland Society's Archive Department and the Museum of English Rural Life at Reading for details on Pollock's stands at various shows. And finally, to the National Trust for Scotland's Robert Smail's Printing Works at Innerleithen for producing new images from old printing blocks.

Jimmy McGhee, April, 2017.

# CHAPTER ONE

# 1867 - 1904 Andrew Pollock

Andrew Pollock was born in the Ayrshire village of Tarbolton in 1841. His father, also Andrew, was described in the 1841 census as a silk handloom weaver, with his wife Euphemia, a Galston lass. They lived in the family home at 46 Montgomerie Street, Tarbolton, along with five brothers and two sisters. Andrew was apprenticed to James Carnduff, the smith at Millburn Smithy. The census of 1861 lists a young Andrew Pollock as being resident in the home of Carnduff. However, with further research being carried out, he is recorded at Midton farm which is almost next door to the smiddy, or smithy, at Millburn.

Millburn Smiddy was well known as a plough, harrow and grubber maker and continued to make these items well after Andrew Pollock left. In February 1874, Carnduff was given a day's ploughing at West Doura farm, normally given at the beginning of a lease, so we can assume that he started farming in 1873/4. The smiddy at Millburn was taken over by Robert Wilson in 1873 to coincide with Carnduff taking the tenancy of West Doura. The farm was at that time on the Duke of Portland's estate.

Carnduff's life was an interesting one. He was recorded at West Doura in the censuses of 1881, 1891 and 1901 along with his daughters and son-in-law John Strathearn, who by 1901 was listed as the head of the family. James Carnduff died on 11 December 1903. His will, written in 1898, names his executors as James Borland (Caldcothill), Robert Wilson (joiner and cartwright, Millburn) and William McMillan (banker in Mauchline). The *Ayr Advertiser* reports a brief obituary of his death:

Obituary: At the close of his sermon on Sabbath last, the Rev William Morgan, MA, Erskine U.F. Church (Tarbolton) made appropriate references to the deceased Mr James Carnduff, farmer (West Doura), who for almost seventy years was an active member of the congregation, for forty years of which he held office as an Elder.

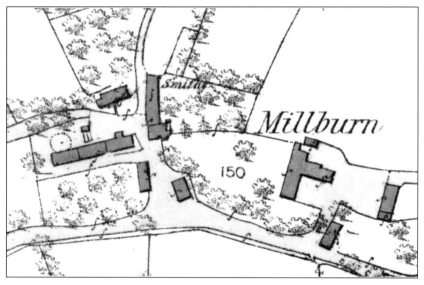

1.01 Millburn Smithy as shown on Ordnance Survey map of 1860

Mr Morgan spoke of him as a man of native talent, indomitable perseverance, transparent and honest and unbending uprightness. He was a man whose life religion entered deeply.

It is also recorded that, in 1893, a clock along with a purse of sovereigns, was presented to James Carnduff by friends and neighbours on his retirement. Since doing my research on James Carnduff/Andrew Pollock, I have now tracked down the very clock presented to James Carnduff – although, there

1.02 Clock presented to James Carnduff

was no sign of the purse or sovereigns! This clock is today the property of Willie Howat of Lawhill farm (near Mauchline), handed down through generations from Carnduff's daughter (he only had daughters) who married John Strathearn. Willie Howat is a direct descendant and is the delighted owner of this trusted time piece.

Andrew Pollock was a good man and was not only taught the engineering skills required to be a successful blacksmith, but also the skill of being honest and upright in his dealings with customers near and far. Andrew Pollock left the employment of Carnduff in 1867 to take over the smiddy of Cowgatehead in Mauchline. After setting up the smiddy in Cowgatehead, he started making several implements including ploughs, hay and straw presses, reaping and mowing machines, potato dressing machines, potato diggers and drill grubbers.

Andrew settled in Mauchline and was married to Janet Logan, a dressmaker, of West Welton farm (Mauchline) on 23 March 1871. Sadly, his life was to be marred with tragedy and the marriage was short-lived, as Janet Pollock died on 19 June 1871. At the time of his wife's death, Andrew Pollock was living at 72 Earl Grey Street in Mauchline. This must have been a very traumatic experience for 29-year-old Andrew and probably why little is heard of Andrew Pollock until 1873.

It was around 1873 that Andrew felt able to return to the agricultural scene. In April of that year, he attended the Ayrshire Agricultural Show. It must have been uplifting for him as this show produced his first success with a medal gained for a single furrow wheel plough with improved bushes. Hard on the heels of this came a medal for a reaping and mowing machine.

In 1875 Pollock took a stand at the Royal Highland Show (Stand Number 135), which exhibited a single furrow wheel plough (Pirie's patent), combined reaping and mowing machine, potato digging machine, single cheese press with compound levers, turnip slicer, monkey for stretching wire fencing and a barrow wheel of iron – an invention which was later to take off.

In 1875, came a medal from The Highland Society for the humble barrow wheel of iron. (This silver medal was to be the last from the Highland Show for 125 years). However, it did not stop Andrew Pollock from building and innovating. He was a strong man who had come from a good family background who believed in hard work, integrity and honesty - something which followed the Pollock family for generations.

The 1876, or 41st, Annual Show of the Ayr Agricultural Association was held at the Cattle Market Park in Ayr with the first day of the show dedicated to the display of implements on hand. This show was undoubtedly second only to the Highland Show. So much was the case that all the leading implement makers in the country wished to exhibit at Ayr.

Over the years, many trials of equipment and implements have been held with the kind permission of various farms. These trials are intricate to the success of any piece of farm work and allow companies the opportunity to see their prototypes in operation and make any adjustments or improvements as necessary.

One such trial took place in 1876 with the Potato Digger Trial which was held at the Glasgow Agricultural Society on 25 October 1876 at Mr Aitkenhead's farm, Shawmoss (Pollockshaws). Many keen agriculturists along with interested bystanders attended these trials. Three diggers were shown by Messrs Kerr (Kilwinning), Andrew Pollock (Mauchline) and John Stoddart (Shettleston). After careful inspection, the prize was awarded to the digger exhibited by Robert Kerr. Although no premium was awarded at Glasgow, Andrew Pollock was adding to his medal collection with medals at both Ayr and Berwick in 1877, 1878/9.

1.03 Potato Dresser of 1879, which could be operated by 'one man and a boy'

On completion of the trials, Thomas Hunter (Maybole) was given the opportunity to show his Patent Turnip Lifter, which created much interest.

That same year, the *Glasgow Herald* reported that a proposal had been tabled that the Association of Implement Makers in the country, with a committee of directors, should search for a piece of ground in a central locality, where shedding of a permanent nature could be erected and where for two or three weeks a year a general exhibition could be held.

These Ayrshire farmers, who had written the letter, had great foresight in proposing the setting up of a National Show Ground centrally located for ease of travel both by exhibitors and public. The article went on to say:

> There is no doubt that the present systems are a great convenience for farmers, as it brings many good implements to their own doors. The proposal, will, however, require ventilation and some years must lapse before it can be carried out, even supposing the preliminary arrangements had been concluded. It the meantime, farmers would continue to use the opportunities placed at their disposal, and nowhere in this district do they possess a better chance than at Ayr.

Suffice to say, the Agricultural Association did not act on this until the Highland Show stopped being a travelling show in 1960, only a mere 84 years after this had been suggested at Ayr!

An advertisement for a potato lifting machine manufactured by Pollock of Mauchline was issued on 5

September 1877. It claimed that the implement was 'the best machine for raising potatoes ever offered to the public. Perfect in work, light and easy to draw. A. Pollock has invented a much lighter machine, with broad-rimmed wrought iron wheels, admirably adapted for moss land or light soil.'

New implements were making ground every year and 1877 was no exception as a new potato dressing machine came on to the market. This was to be a show stopper, winning not only the First Prize medal at the United East Lothian Show in North Berwick, First Prize Silver Medal at Long Sutton Agricultural Society Show, September 1878, but also First Prize Silver Medal at Northumberland Agricultural Society Show in July 1879.

The young but eager Andrew Pollock by this time had truly arrived on the Agricultural Scene. His advert stated:

> Andrew Pollock has much pleasure in submitting to Potato Merchant Farmers, his new Potato Dressing or Separating Machine, for preparing for market or taking out seconds for seeds. Andrew Pollock can with confidence recommend them as being the best machine ever brought into the market.
>
> With one man and a boy, they are capable of dressing one ton of potatoes per hour into the different sizes, large, seconds and small. The price for a machine complete with double bottom and two riddles - £4 10s 0d, carriage paid.

As the Ayr Show came around, Andrew Pollock decided to exhibit a new two-horse Mower and Reaper. With two speeds, this machine was used to suit the crops with two hilt heck – one for seed hay and one for grain. It also had a

1.04 The 'Land o' Burns' Patent Potato Digger of 1886

swather for meadow hay. By the late 1870's, Andrew Pollock was acting as an agent for superior chaff cutters, the best maker of root pulpers, slicers, meat coolers, sack barrows, barrel churns, and fanners and winnowers.

Due to the competitive nature of the industry and competitors making similar machines to Andrew Pollock's Potato Dressing Machine of 1877, which as we know had won many medals and prizes up and down the country, it would disappear from production around 1888.

At the Highland Show of 1879, Stand Number 133 showed a vastly improved Pollock line up from the initial Highland Show in 1875, which had a total of nine machines on show.

In 1878, Andrew Pollock exhibited no fewer than three potato diggers, one heavy machine on cast iron wheels, one medium weight digger with wrought iron wheels and one light potato digger with broad rimmed wrought iron wheels to suit moss land, as well as a combined turnip topping and tailing machine which converted into a potato digger.

20

The year 1879 saw no fewer than twenty machines on show, including three types of potato digger, two types of two-horse thrashing machines, two potato dressers, combined reaper and mower with stubble rake, washing and wringing machine with mangle, curd mill, drill harrow with front wheels, drill grubber with steel lines, monkey wire stretcher, lever for lifting carts and barrel churns, pulpers, slicers and strippers. From Richardson (Carlisle) and Corbett and Peel (Shrewsbury), Thrashing Machines were made to order on the newest principles known. Engines and boilers of all kinds both new and second hand.

Alongside the growth of the business was a blossoming personal life for Andrew, now 37, who found happiness once again marrying farmer's daughter Martha Jamieson from West Welton. Incidentally, this was the same farm he had taken his first wife from in 1871. This marriage was to last until Andrew Pollock's death in 1904 and by all accounts was an extremely happy one.

The company continue to see opportunity for growth and in 1879 saw further expansion into two-horse thrashing machines with strong fans. Thrashing machines did not figure as prominently as potato diggers, drill grubbers and curd mills which Andrew Pollock was beginning to earn his reputation from. Even though thrashing machines were made locally by George McCartney (Cumnock), it made good business sense for Andrew Pollock to continue to manufacture both two-horse and improved three-horse thrashing machines until 1886.

The 1880s proved to be an extremely tough time for agriculture in Scotland with a severe depression in farming. Andrew Pollock advertised in the *Ayr Advertiser*:

> Andrew Pollock begs to remind those requiring
> Potato Digger Machines this season that they will

be so kind as to send in their orders as soon as is
convenient, so that they may be attended to
before the great pressure of the season comes on.
This season's machines are further improved and
a liberal discount to ready money purchases will
be given.

Ayr Show in 1880 saw a premium being awarded to Andrew
Pollock for a large collection of implements at the county
exhibition. Andrew Pollock showed amongst them a
thrashing mill with riddle, elevator and fans, potato raiser and
riddle, ploughs, rollers, harrows and a hay collector, all well
made.

From the archives, we find the first mention of hay
collectors in 1881, along with double-bottomed potato
dressing machines, which divided potatoes into three
different sizes at once. By 1883, this machine had been greatly
improved to now house an oscillating bottom screen fitted for
the removal of soil.

It should be noted that when the Highland Show visited
Stirling in 1778, there were only twenty-two machines on
show. Fast forward to 1864 and there were 1,000 implements
on show and in 1881, the total reached 2,000. There were 209
ordinary implements in the Motion Yard. One of the more
interesting machines on display was the all-steel frame and
wrought iron grubber with large wheels.

The year 1882 saw the introduction of Pollock's Superior
land rollers of thirty inch and thirty-three inch diameters.
These also sold well and many examples survive some 130
years later. Also on show was zig zag and chain harrows,
turnip mangold and carrot sowers and cheese presses.

In March 1883, in the *West Country Journal* an advert
appeared:

> Andrew Pollock begs to intimate that he is now
> suppling his Superior Land Roller, size of
> cylinders 30" and 33" diameter, all run on brass
> bushes at still further reduced prices. Zig Zag
> Harrows and Chain Harrows, Turnip, Mangold
> and Carrot Sower and Curd Mills and Cheese
> Presses.

From extensive research, I find no evidence of the existence of a Pollock foundry although in 1884, adverts were placed in several newspapers looking for a pattern maker. However, it is commonplace even today for manufacturers to own all the patterns and supply these to the various foundries to be used. Pollocks used many foundries for a variety of jobs. Some of the popular foundries used were James Dickie (Ayr), Cruickshank's (Denny), Comleybank (Denny), Simpson's (Hurlford), F. W. Birkett (Cleckheaton), The Vulcan Foundry (Hurlford) and of course some of the largest foundries, H. Bamford & Son (Uttoxeter), Jones & Campbell (Larbert), George Taylor (Hamilton) and Arthur McLuckie & Son (Dalry).

The preparations for the 1885 Highland Show held in Aberdeen in July of that year were well underway. With regards to the agricultural Implement department of the show, it is interesting to note that:

> … premiums of £20 and £10 were offered for …
> the most efficient and economical implement to
> be drawn by horses on strong turnip land by
> ploughing, digging, stirring or in any way
> thoroughly moving the soil and which leaves it
> in spring in the most suitable state of preparation
> for the ensuing turnip crop.

To be judged at the time when the work is performed in autumn and the following March or April, before the land is touched again.

The following have entered the competition:

J. Allan & Son (Dunkeld)
W. Craig (Inverurie)
Thomas Corbett (Shrewsbury)
J. Bisset & Sons (Blairgowrie)
Lankester & Co (London)
MacDonald Bros (Portsoy)
G. W. Murray (Banff)
Andrew Pollock (Mauchline)
I. Scott (Bonnybridge)
G. Sellars & Co (Huntly)
John Scoular (Stirling)
Wm. Webster (Fyvie)
and David Whitecross (Banff)


This competition was of great importance to Andrew Pollock as his stand at Aberdeen comprised of a drill grubber with five tines, drill grubber with three tines, a three-horse cultivator and three-horse grubber. No premium was awarded to Andrew Pollock on this occasion.

It was clear that farmers were the forefront of any stand exhibition Andrew made. In the same year, well known Ayrshire cattle breeder and exhibitor, Mr Robert Wardrop, Garlaff farm (Skares, near Cumnock) showed his bulls with 'Gallant Lad' taking first prize among the three-year olds and gaining third spot in the same class with 'King of Kyle'. Robert Wardrop was known to be a regular visitor to Mauchline and on one occasion, prior to arriving at Mauchline, he delivered 47 bushels of corn to Ochiltree mill for bruising. His diary entry also states that an Australian farmer had visited him to purchase two Ayrshire cows and one bull before going on to Drumfork (Auchinleck) to purchase more Ayrshire cattle.

Pollock's prominent Land of Burns Potato Digger came to market in 1885. This upgraded system saw the addition of closed gears instead of open gears, vastly improving the life of this machine.

The inauguration meeting of Mauchline Liberal Association covered by the *Ardrossan and Saltcoats Herald* in November 1885, highlighted how well thought of Andrew Pollock was, citing: 'a large and enthusiastic crowd greeted Andrew Pollock, implement maker on to the Platform'. The same newspaper further reported that Mauchline's new United Presbyterian Church had appointed Andrew Pollock as contractor for the railings surrounding the church.

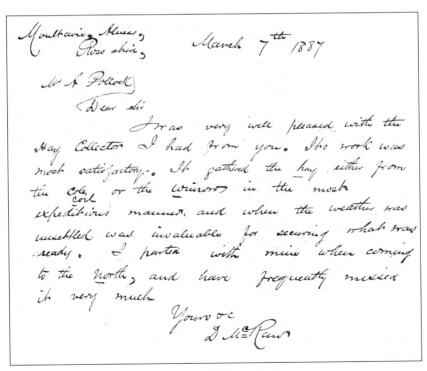

1.05 Letter from an 1887 satisfied customer

The depression was to have an impact on the business and in 1886, Stand 27, was to be a much smaller affair. Andrew Pollock exhibited for the first time his Land of Burns Patent Potato Digger which like all previous machines sold well. Thankfully, by 1887, the depression which hit farmers and implement makers appeared to be almost over with farm incomes up on previous years.

The new Glenbuck turnip cutter was introduced to the farming scene in 1887. It was sold on the premise that it could be carried about by a shepherd. One can only imagine that these shepherds were hardy men indeed.

Shows and exhibitions proved to be pivotal in the Pollock success, being a platform to promote and cultivate new business and show off the many implements available or coming to market.

The 1888 Highland Show was no different with Andrew Pollock exhibiting a curd mill, a new and improved baling machine with wheels, shafts and top doors and a new machine for shifting hay ricks from the field to hayshed without forking. This exhibition at the Glasgow Highland Show would certainly take some beating.

That same year, eager to secure his products, Andrew Pollock applied for a patent for his curd mill (used in the production of cheese). This curd mill is a simple but effective machine and sold in large numbers - so much so that I have two machines in my collection today.

Pollock's Stand Number 39 at the Glasgow show that year housed several combined reapers and sowers, drill grubbers, ploughs and a variety of sack and hay barrows. A hay baling machine was also on view at this stand. It was said to be capable of being worked by a mere boy, in every way serviceable and exceedingly cheap at £15 0s 0d.

The curd mill, which was patented in October 1888, was still to be in production over forty years later.  On the letters patent 9see the Appendix), it states:

> This Curd Mill is an improvement on all others
> by replacing the pegs, which were normally
> made from wood, either square or round, to be
> replaced by round or oval pegs of Iron.

At the same show, Andrew Pollock also exhibited his new hay or straw barrow made of wrought iron.  The barrows became the standard method of feeding hay or straw for the next fifty years.

At the 1888 Ayr Show, it was of great concern to manufacturers and exhibitors that the long depression in the trade and the want of money in the farming community would greatly reduce the number of visitors.  In fact, the 1888 International Exhibition in Glasgow was thought to have had little or no impact on Ayr Show.  Stand Number 44 had a large collection of Andrew Pollock implements including the improved 'Land of Burns' potato digger, patented curd mills, grubbers and ploughs.

Andrew Pollock took great care when designing and implementing new machinery and equipment and this is one of the reasons why in 1889, very few new implements were on show with the only item listed as new being Land Rollers with 30 inch and 33 inch cylinders and a Large Grubber or Cultivator.  Earlier, I mentioned a rick lifter for which a patent had been applied for, and by 1889 this had been granted.  Further development of this led to the new improved rick lifter for horse power. It was also available for hand power.  Another interesting development was that of a new hay collector which could gather one ton of hay, also listed in the

1890 Highland Show catalogue along with what was now his standard offerings.

The 1889 Highland Show visited Melrose for the first time. At the show, held around 65 miles east of Mauchline, Andrew Pollock had no fewer than twenty implements on display including his improved Hay Baling Machine with wheels, shafts and top doors, curd mills, cheese press to hold two large cheeses, drill plough with improved index markers, elevating sack barrows which had been improved over time and were still sold right up to the 1960s.

At Melrose, the premiums being offered were for hay and stand trussers and hand baling machines. The competitors in this class were:

Messrs Thomas Aimers & Sons (Galashiels)
Andrew Pollock (Mauchline)
Richard & Chandler (Manchester)
John Turnbull & Son (Larbert)
John Scoular (Stirling)

The rules laid down at the competition were as follows:

Each machine be portable, hand operated and capable of making a truss from 1½ cwt to 2¼ cwt.

At the end of the trials, the Judges opted for the machine put forward by John Turnbull & Son of Larbert.

Never to be downhearted and undeterred, Andrew Pollock entered his new machine for the Gold Medal at the 1891 United East Lothian Show at Haddington and was judged to be the equal winner of this competition with Turnbull & Son.

Diversity was the essence in 1891 with new hay collector, rick lifters, land rollers, Sinton's patent prize winning churns, and a Hunter hoe (made by Thomas Hunter (Maybole). A totally new piece of equipment came to market this year which was a departure from the norm for Andrew Pollock and that was a garden seat with polished pitch pine. These were made by the cartwrights and blacksmiths in time of need and were in fact used as a resting place for many customers attending the various shows. Two of the seats were used up until the 1970s.

The business and Pollock's efforts to display award winning pieces of equipment carried on and in 1893 a parallel lifting grubber on high wheels, galvanised food cooler, horse rakes and hay tedder by W. Nicholson & Son Ltd, chaff cutters, cake mills and self binders were all approved for display and sale by Andrew Pollock.

Andrew's skill for innovation continued with the patent of what would surely be his most ingenious and innovative machine to date. The combined land roller and broadcast seed sower came to market and was well received.

The Highland Show stands grew along with the number of implements on display and at the 1894 show some thirty implements were on display, of which twenty-two were Andrew Pollock manufactured. We have heard plenty of mention of A. Jack & Co (Maybole), but for the first time they were exhibited on Pollock's stand, with their dux plough for ploughing lea, stubble or fallow land, being unrivalled.

Dumfries played host to the Highland Show in July 1895, which being approximately fifty miles from Mauchline appeared almost a local show for Andrew Pollock. A *Glasgow Herald* journalist described the display of implements at the Highland Society Show as one of the largest and most attractive collection of implements shown in Scotland. The *Glasgow Herald* feature was a positive report on Andrew

Pollock and his business and showed his great tenacity and business prowess:

> Mr Andrew Pollock, Mauchline, shows several of his specialities. His Potato Diggers for which there has been a great demand have been further improved with the addition of a pole in place of the front wheel whilst the centre wheel and axle have benefited from case hardening for durability.
>
> There is also the improved Hay & Straw Press (Baling Machine) for which Andrew Pollock was awarded a Gold Medal at the Haddington Show. It is arranged in such a manner to allow a lad to prepare it for transport, one minute after the men stop baling. Andrew Pollock patented 1894 Combined Land Roller & Grass & Clover Seed Sower has turned out to be a great success. The machine sows and rolls at the same time and the seed falling in front of the roller. It further acts as a distributer of fertiliser. Also on show was the patented Rick Lifter. In addition, a selection of Reaping & Mowing Machines, Curd Mills, Cheese Presses, Drill Ploughs & Grubbers.

Throughout the year, Andrew looked for ways to enhance the business by working partnerships and appointing companies who could bring something new to the table. One such company was T. & J. McErvel, 40 Victoria Square (Belfast) who were appointed in 1895 as Irish Agents. They held this position until they ceased trading, sometime in the 1940s. Also, mentioned in the *Belfast Newsletter* is the smaller version of the hay float (rick lifter), the midget haymaker. It was reported to be...

...the most perfect of its kind taking one swath at
a time. The shafts are so constructed that the
pony which draws this machines does not walk
on the hay.

In 1895, new implements were scarce and Andrew Pollock
lists a two row Curd Mill, a three row Curd Mill and Horse
Gear for a Horse Driven Churn used in the production of
butter. Despite the lack of new implements, Andrew revisited
the old, making improvements in Drill Grubbers with three
weights of these now being offered.

Distance was often an issue for display and exhibits and
this may well account for the 1896 Highland Show whose
catalogue records a mere fifteen implements being on display.
Despite the quantity of goods, it remained clear that the
quality was the driving factor and would always outweigh the
number on show.

Many articles have been written over the years regarding
Andrew Pollock and predecessors. One such article in the 6
July 1897 edition of *The Scotsman* records that:

Andrew Pollock (Mauchline) shows a very good
selection of labour saving devices and it may be
mentioned so great is the demand for the
machines of this prominent Ayrshire maker. A
very good and substantial combined Reaper and
Mower of a new style, with a tilting board for
hay and corn is one of the features of this stand.

There was disappointment surrounding the 1897 Royal
Agricultural Show which took place in June of that year. It is
noted that the Special Correspondent reported that:

31

> Display of implements from the Scottish
> Manufacturers did not reveal anything of
> importance.

The usual companies were represented including Messrs Wallace (Glasgow), A. Jack (Maybole). T. Hunter (Maybole), Gray (Stranraer), P. & W. McLellan (Glasgow), John S. Millar (Annan), Nobel Explosive Company, Andrew Pollock (Mauchline) and Ben Reid (Aberdeen).

Disappointment or not, the Andrew Pollock patent hay collector was shown at the Royal Show at Manchester on 23 June 1897, alongside a small but interesting show of mowing, reaping machines and potato diggers. The 1897 Highland Show mentions Nicholson's patent switchback hay turner which Andrew Pollock introduced to Ayrshire. Also on show was a new double cheese press and a patent curd mill of the type used by the Dairy School, Kilmarnock.

At the Highland Show in 1897, it was recorded:

> Andrew Pollock (Mauchline) shows a very good
> collection of labour saving appliances and it may
> be mentioned that many of the products of this
> firm have already been booked, so great is the
> demand for the machines from this prominent
> Ayrshire maker. A very good substantial
> combined Reaper and Mower of new a style with
> a tilting board for hay and corn is one of the
> features on this stand. Practical agriculturalists
> should make a pause at this exhibit.

The same year saw the first mention of Pollock carts, which were to form a major part of the companies output for many years to come.

A medal was next step in the journey for Andrew as he was awarded this at the 1899 Northumberland Show for his new patented hay collector. Although the show is normally a county show, because of its proximity to the Border, it also has an interest for many Scottish agriculturists who were regular visitors to the area.

Andrew's business had progressed considerably by this time, having reached a landmark of having exhibited at the Highland Show for a quarter of a century. He used the last show of the nineteenth century to display his new farm cart and his coup cart. The following year, 1900, his new 'Ayrshire' long-bodied cart was on show, complete with harvest sides.

1.06 The Dairy School for Scotland at Kilmarnock

Scotland represented themselves well at the Royal Show at York on 18 June 1900. The Special Correspondent who reported on the lack of Scottish Exhibitors in Manchester noted that:

Three years on and a new century later,
exhibitors from North of the Tweed were to be
found in numbers fully up to the average.

It is easy to see how the enthusiasm for the business could catch you as Andrew never gave up and continued to research and put new ideas on to the table. He was determined to make a success of the business north and south of the border.

The year 1902 saw Andrew exhibiting twenty machines on his stand, with the Nicholson's haymaker and the washing machine and wringer (Craig's patent) being the only machines not built by Andrew Pollock. I feel this is due to the location of the Highland Show which was held in Dumfries.

It was decision time for Andrew who decided to take on the English based manufacturers in their own back yard by booking stand space at the Smithfield Show in London.

Eagerness grew and Andrew Pollock went to Smithfield show which was held at Islington in 1903 but, due to a shortage of stand space, Andrew Pollock occupied a small stand in the minor hall of the building exhibiting a tipping farm cart, various cultivators and grindstones. This rocky start did not deter him and he returned to Smithfield year on year thereafter.

The Highland Show moved on to Dumfries for 1903's exhibition and the report from the show stated:

1.07 Ayrshire Pattern cart of around 1899

1.08 Pollock's Hay Cart of c. 1899

> No exhibition of implements connected with the
> National Show would be complete without the
> stand of Andrew Pollock (Mauchline).
> Agricultural machinery of his make is noted for
> good quality of material and sound character of
> workmanship. He has brought to this show an
> admirable collection of his goods.

The same year saw the first mention of Pollock carts, which were to form a major part of the company's output for many years to come. Also produced was a cart which was sold as a 'bakers' van'.

The year 1904 saw Andrew Pollock show his usual large display of implements including his potato dressing machines which had been modified, his hay press of 1891 which was still current, curd mills, potato diggers and farm carts. A new design of farm cart was made for the Irish Market which was marketed by T. & J. McErvel (Belfast).

In Pollock's sales brochure, it boasted that the frame of this cart was made from best seasoned oak and was lined throughout with best redwood larch. It was fitted with a double self-acting lock. The naves were of best scotch elm, spokes of best home grown oak and the fellows of ash. The axles were of the best scrap iron laid with steel and case hardened to ensure smooth and easy running.

The prices were as follows:

| | | |
|---|---|---|
| Tipping Cart | (No. 1) | £15 0s 0d |
| Fast Body | (No. 1) | £14 10s 0d |
| Set Loose Sides | (No. 2) | 17s 0d |
| Harvest Frames | | £1 6s 0d |
| Set of Strong Chain | | 7s 0d |

1.09 Baker's van of c. 1900

The Perth Highland Show stand number seven, in 1904, housed Andrew Pollock's usual display of twenty or so implements. It had a Nicholson haymaker, Craig's washing machine and Deering ideal harvester were the only non 'Pollock' implements on show.

The Highland Show with no new products went well with many existing customers and new customers. Alas this was to be Andrew Pollock's last exhibition as he died on his sleep on 1 October 1904 aged 64.

It was recorded in his obituary:

Mr Andrew Pollock, the well-known Agricultural Implement Maker, died following a coaching tour to Ballantrae along with friends, which he seemed to enjoy very much and returned in good health. However, around 5 o'clock in the morning, he had deceased.

37

Andrew Pollock left behind a widow, Martha Jamieson, who was to run the business on behalf of her family until her sons Andrew and William had finished schooling and could take over from their mother.

Andrew Pollock had left a legacy for his children. These were, Mary Humphrey (b. 1883 - d. 4 May 1929); Andrew, who died in childhood on 24 February 1885; the second Andrew (b. 1888) - it appears commonplace in Victorian times that if a child died, the next born would inherit the same name; a sister Euphemia (b. 1885 - d. 20 December 1929); Alexander John MBChB, D.Ph. (died at Stoke on Trent 28 March 1953); and Martha (b. 1880).

Shortly after the death of Andrew Pollock, the notice below was printed in the *Ayr Advertiser*:

> 5th October 1904. All persons having claims against the late Andrew Pollock, Agricultural Engineer, Mauchline, are requested to lodge the same with the subscribers within 14 days from this date.
>
> D. & J. Dunlop, Solicitors, Agents for the Deceased, Trustees and Executors. Regarding the above notice, the Trustees of the late Mr Andrew Pollock desire to intimate that the well-known business carried out by him at Mauchline will be continued under experienced management for the benefit of the widow and family. All orders will receive the strict attention and will be executed with the same promptitude and thoroughness in the time of the Mr Andrew Pollock.

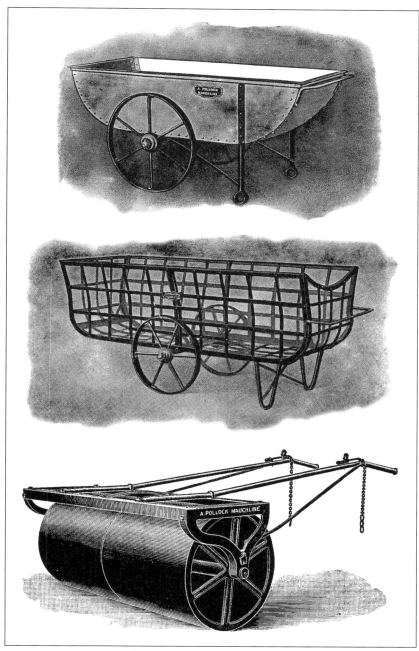

1.10 Early products – Food Cooler, 1894 (top),
Hay or Straw Barrow (middle), Land Roller, 1891 (bottom)

1.11 Turnip Slicers

1.12 Letterhead of Andrew Pollock

Throughout his life, Andrew Pollock had introduced many patents and new designs for a host of implements. However, he never closed his eyes to the innovations all around him, as can be seen from the implements available from his competitors. As we can be fathomed from the list of implements displayed on his stands from 1875-1904, the top machines and manufacturers were represented. He was an honoured man with a business to be proud of and left behind a legacy which would speak of him for many years to come.

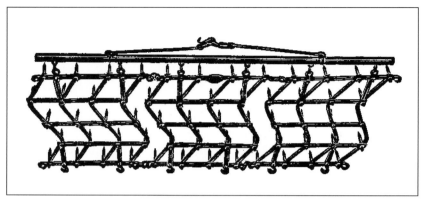

1.13 Zig Zag Harrows from 1882

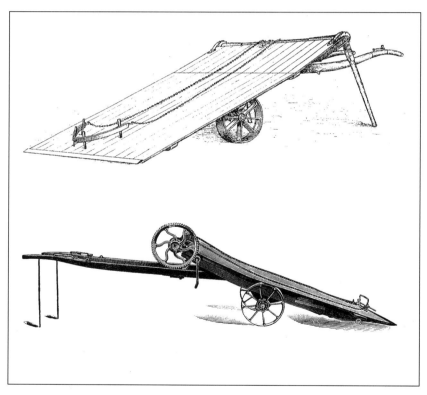

1.14 Rick Lifter of 1891 (top), Rick Lifter of 1889, powered by horse (bottom)

# CHAPTER TWO

# 1904-1914 Martha Pollock

Life had to continue and Martha Pollock, along with her management team, continued the work of her late husband. In 1904, Pollock's visited, for the second time, Smithfield Show. On this occasion, they exhibited farm carts, potato diggers and drill grubbers.

The Royal Ulster show in 1905 saw the usual companies, A. Jack & Sons (Maybole), Thomas Hunter & Sons (Maybole), Andrew Pollock (Mauchline) and Messrs Wallace (Glasgow), exhibit. This exhibition was the show's jubilee and on Thursday 12 May, the most expensive day, it was reported:

> The picturesque showground at Balmoral was filled with a fashionably dressed throng, consequently, there was a large turnout of the aristocracy and the beautiful costumes of the ladies added brightness to the natural surroundings.

By the time the Highland Show came around in 1905, Stand 28 was allocated to Andrew Pollock and it was almost all dedicated to exhibit Andrew Pollock wares. In fact, only the Nicholson's new switchback haymaker and Deering & Company's 'Ideal' harvester were presented that was not produced by them.

The potato digger of 1885 was vastly improved in 1906, by removing the front wheel and replacing it with a pole. Their patent rick lifter, now with a patented rope guard, was also present. Again, other manufacturers' machines were on display including Nicholson's new 'Snapdragon' rake and Deering's binder.

2.01 A selection of implements made by Thomas Hunter of Maybole taken in 1904.

In 1907, an interesting article appears in *The Scotsman*. It stated that the Pollock Patent rick lifter was now available for either hand or horse power.

Andrew Pollock had not exhibited a combined reaper and mower since 1905. However, it made a brief comeback in 1908. By then Andrew Pollock and Deering & Co were now offering their binders.

Now firmly on the scene and run by the late Andrew's wife and her trusted team, Andrew Pollock were offered a bigger stand in the main hall at the 1908 Smithfield Show, this time the collection of implements included hay and straw baler, tipping cart, and grubbers. The show report also stated that Andrew Pollock took many orders from the south of England at this show.

2.02 Hay and Straw Baler of c. 1900 (top) and
Hercules Hay Baler of c. 1912 (bottom)

By 1909, the end was nigh for the combined reaper and mower, but its place in the field of harvesting was assured. In that year, Pollock started the development of their Pollock 'Perfect' potato digger which, when exhibited at Smithfield Show in 1909, caused a stir amongst other exhibitors and agriculturists.

The 1910, the *Derry Journal* records:

> The Department of Agriculture and County Tyrone Committee of Agriculture were present when a novel and most interesting potato digging trial took place at Urney, the home of Mr J. Elliot, a short distance from Strabane.
>
> The objective of the demonstration was to allow farmers to form their own opinion on the best machine on trial suitable for their own farm. The turnout was a revelation as to the perfection to

2.03 Pollock's 'Perfect' Potato Digger

which the Potato Digger had been brought and the expedition with which an extensive crop can be dealt with.

The eight entries were:

Messrs Bamford (Uttoxeter) with their machine 'Triumph'
Alex Jack & Sons with their 'Caledonian'
Andrew Pollock with the 'Pollock Perfect Potato Digger' with its all-steel frame
Messrs Powell Bros & Whittaker (Wrexham) with two machines, namely their 'Cambrian and 'Newcastle'
Ransomes Sims & Jeffries, again with two entries,
Geo Sellars & Son with one machine
J. Bisset (Blairgowrie) with one machine.

In 1910, the major items were Pollock's hay collector and the potato digger, the latter of which was fast gaining a reputation for being light in draught and robust in performance. This report was in the annual *Implement and Machinery Review*, which also commented on good sales of potato diggers in Ireland.

The Royal Show returned to Norwich in July 1911 after an absence of a quarter of a century. The implement trade north of the border was well represented, with three Ayrshire companies who had been exhibited at the Royal for half a century, namely A. Jack, T. Hunter and Andrew Pollock.

As trials had become just as important as the implement themselves, the Highland & Agricultural Society decided in 1911 that since it was now forty years since a potato digging trial had been organised by them, the time was ripe for calling another event. This culminated in the trial being set up at Turnhouse, by kind permission of Mr James Stenhouse.

With exceptionally good weather at the 'back-end', a large crowd of farmers, potato merchants, trades people and the well know aristocrat, Lord Ninian Crichton-Stuart, all attended this spectacle.

The appointed judgers were:


T. Malcom (Larbert)
Mr McHutcheon (Dalkeith)
Mr Dun (Auchtermuchty)
John Edmond (Bannockburn)
Professor Stanfield of Heriot Watt, the
Engineering Advisor to the Society.


There were fourteen machines entered in the competition. The entries were subject to the rules laid down at the Highland Show in Inverness. The firms which entered were:


J. D. Allan & Son (Murthly) – two machines
A. Ballach & Son (Leith)
J. Bisset & Sons
Martin's Cultivation Co Ltd (Stamford) – two machines
Ransomes Sims & Jeffries – two machines
Andrew Pollock (Mauchline) – 'Perfect Potato Digger'
Powell Bros & Whittaker – two machines
George Wallace & Sons (Glasgow)
David Wilson (East Linton)

2.04 Fast Body Cart

However, on the day only five machines were on trial, namely:

J. D. Allan & Son (Murthly) – 2 machines
Andrew Pollock (Mauchline)
George Wallace & Sons (Glasgow)
David Wilson (East Linton)

The most noticeable absentee was that of the first prize winning machine at the Royal Agricultural Society England, namely Martin's Cultivation Company.

The trials got under way at around 8 am and each competitor had to lift six drills each of 160 yards long complete with 'shaws' and six drills with cut shaws. The soil was of an extremely free loam, quite sandy in fact, and did not offer any serious difficulty to the five machines on trial. After completing two drills of 160 yards, a basketful of potatoes was gathered from a selected point and counted, together with the number of damaged potatoes. The results were recorded:

Allan (No. 1) digger:
248 potatoes were in the basket with 14 described as damaged.

Allan (No. 2) digger:
295 potatoes were in the basket with 7 described as damaged.

Wallace's digger:
312 potatoes were in the basket with 20 described as damaged.

Andrew Pollock's digger:
310 potatoes were in the basket with 15 described as damaged.

Mr Stenhouse then demonstrated his old Wallace Digger which acquitted itself admirably:
324 potatoes were in the basket with 34 described as damaged.

Considering the results from each potato digger and the similarity of performance, it was decided that each of the five diggers on trial would be awarded a prize of ten guineas. Mr Paton then intimated that a full report on this demonstration would be available before the next committee meeting.

It was then left to Mr Paton to propose a hearty vote of thanks to Mr Stenhouse for allowing this demonstration. These demonstrations served as a great opportunity to meet other farmers and share knowledge and form lasting friendships.

After the Highland Agricultural Potato Trials (1911), Pollock Perfect Potato Digger was very much in demand, especially in Ireland with Pollock's agent T. & J. McErvel. The *Belfast Weekly News* on 30 May 1912 reported:

2.05 A selection of carts produced by Pollock's.

2.06 Harvest Cart with Ladders.

The Royal Ulster Agricultural Show at Balmoral was generally larger than ever before and Pollock's Agent, T. & J. McErvel Limited, had more than kept pace with the times and has made the finest exhibits of any one house. The Pollock Perfect Potato Digger made of the German principal but suited to this country where wider and deeper drills are made is the star attraction.

The massive crowds at Balmoral also turned out for the Royal Dublin Society Show at Ballsbridge where 17 Scottish exhibitors are largely in evidence. Firms being representative include Mr Andrew Pollock with his Rick Lifters, Land Rollers, Baling Machines and Potato Diggers.

The following year, 1912, at Smithfield Show, Andrew Pollock unveiled his new 'Hercules' hay baler which by all accounts was well received. The price was £12 0s 0d for a one hundredweight baler and £13 10s 0d for a one and a half hundredweight baler.

The Royal Dublin Society Show in July of that year reports:

> Among the many exhibitors showing their wares, the Scottish implement trade is well represented.

This fashion continued at Ballsbridge in Dublin in 1913, with exhibits crowding the entire Central Hall with all available stand space having been over-applied for. The years 1913, 1914 and 1915, saw record exports to Ireland, not only potato diggers but the lifting of hay, with the company's improved rick lifter enjoying the largest sale of any rick lifter in the kingdom. This was partly due to it being the simplest and easiest to work for man and horse, and of course, it was built on the best lines.

Another local company who were making inroads into the buoyant Irish market was George McCartney & Company, Cumnock, who were selling their threshing machines, one of large range of implements they manufactured.

> The Paisley Highland Show in 1913 recorded the following prices:

> Mower and reaper (made by Albion) sold for £15 0s 0d.
> The Pollock Perfect potato digger was also £15 0s 0d
> Pollock patent rick lifter with Patent rope guard £10 0s 0d.
> Pollock patent rick lifter for horse power £11 0s 0d.

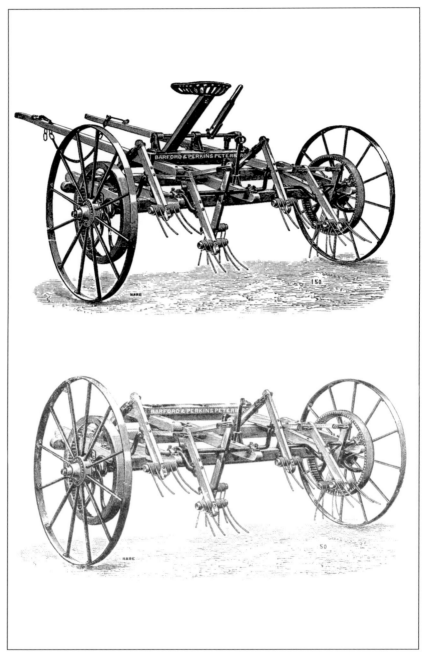

2.07 Barford and Perkins Tedders, c. 1913

Pollock patent rick lifter - sides for carrying stock
£12 0s 0d.
Hay and straw press to make one
hundredweight bale £12 0s 0d.
Hay and straw press to make one and a half
hundredweight bale £13 10s 0d.
Wheels and shafts, and wheels to suit balers
£3 0s 0d.
Double cheese press £6 10s 0d.
Single cheese press £3 15s 0d.
Patent curd mill no. 2 £3 5s 0d.
Patent curd mill no. 3 £3 15s 0d.
Cart no. A4 with 2½" tyres £14 10s 0d.
Cart no. B4 with 4" tyres £15 10s 0d.
Ayrshire harvest cart with 2½" tyres £13 10s 0d.
MSD horse rakers by Nicholson £28 0s 0d.
Deering Ideal harvester £28 0s 0d.
Bisset steel binder £27 10s 0d.
New potato sorter £10 0s 0d.
Hay tedder (Barford Perkins) £13 0s 0d.


It should be noted that in 1913, the Combined Mower &
Reaper was dropped in favour of the Albion Reaper. Thus,
'The Ideal' ended a production run of some forty years.

# CHAPTER THREE

# 1914-1939 Andrew & William Pollock (I)

Martha Pollock coped well with the business but took the decision around 1914 to relinquish the reigns of the company to her two sons, Andrew and William Pollock. From that date onward the company was known as A. & W. Pollock. The company A. & W. Pollock had purchased a site adjacent to Mauchline station where a 15,000-square foot manufacturing plant was erected. This had a brand new Tangye engine installed to power the many machines which were not driven by electric motors, complete with wood curing shed, steel shed and a large retail store.

The implement work was fabricated and erected by A. & J. Main & Co who for many years acted as agent for A. & W. Pollock. The superstructure was of 'H' beams with angle iron and flat bar for the trusses. There was not a single weld in the building. Every joint was made with fillet plates and rivets. The roof was of a wooden construction covered by slate.

The single storey office was divided into two which would serve as home for the typist and Ian Bryan and a private office for Andrew and William Pollock, complete with a fire safe and toilet facilities.

This was perfect for the job until 1968 when a second storey was added with John Pollock occupying one office and a new drawing office, with the former drawing office being demolished to give more floor space.

As usual, when things are going well, there is always something on the horizon. This time it was of a more serious nature – World War 1. On 28 June 1914, with the assassination of Franz Ferdinand, Austria-Hungry declared war on Serbia.

By August that year, Germany declared war on France and soon afterwards, we were plunged into war.

The last show attended prior to the First World War being declared was the show in Londonderry, a mere five days before the start of hostilities. The County Antrim Agricultural Association Show held the week before noted that T. & J. McErvel had a very attractive exhibit of an almost endless variety of implements and machine which, the changing conditions demanded, should be used on the up to date farms. These implements were all mainly the manufacture of Andrew Pollock.

The wartime records of A. & W. Pollock are not available, although in the price list of Farm Carts 1904, on the front cover, it boasts, 'Contractor to His Majesty's Government' and 'Contractor to the Government of the French Republic'. We know from this that they supplied both governments, but we have no idea of which machines or quantities. However, during the war, A. & W. Pollock are thought to have manufactured munitions carts for the Government. However, no Ministry of War records were available.

3.01 Pollock's Contractor's Cart.

Just prior to moving from Cowgatehead in 1915, the old factory, which housed a garage and a storage shed, caught fire around 7.00 o'clock in the evening. Mauchline Fire Brigade were summoned and luckily there was an ample supply of water and the blaze was soon extinguished. A new motor car, which had been purchased a few days earlier, was destroyed in the blaze.

Due to the war effort, tradesmen were sparse and on 5 February 1915, the *Dumfries and Galloway Standard* had an advert for blacksmith and cartwrights, offering a 'Good wage to suitable men'.

Obviously, the shortage of trades-people was due entirely to the war. This interruption had affected A. & W. Pollock but not to a major degree. There was still a thriving show scene in Ireland, albeit greatly scaled down from pre-war years.

The *Derry Journal*, 5 July 1916, reports:

> At the showrooms of William Thomson & Co
> Ltd, this most eminent firm, the following
> amongst other implements of first class make can
> be expected.
> G. McCartney – Thrashing Mill,
> A. & W. Pollock – Rick Lifters etc.

A. & W. Pollock did not attend another show until after the war.

In 1916, various adverts were placed in local and national newspapers:

> Blacksmiths for implements and Cartwright
> work; good wages to suitable men. Apply A. &
> W. Pollock, Mauchline.

The years 1915-16 proved to be a very busy time for the Pollock Brothers moving plant and equipment from Cowgatehead to Station Road one piece at a time but still manufacturing at both sites.

The full transfer of the business from Cowgatehead to Station Road was undertaken in 1916. Some of the machines which were made in the 1890s-1900 were hauled downhill to Station Road, a distance of 500-600 yards. One such machine was a large vertical drill manufactured by Charles Swift (Halifax, Yorkshire) and Gilmour Milton informed me that it took some eight men to load and transfer the drill onto a station barrow.

The new workshop was now ready for production with around 15,000 square feet of manufacturing area. To the left-hand side of the building there were five smiddy fires along the length of the workshop, a railway track and a travelling four-wheel bogie with a four-inch-thick blacksmith's table with various squares holes and round holes to suit the tool the blacksmiths had selected for a specific job.

The next bay was the machine shop equipped with a centre lathe made by J. Loudoun (Glasgow), a turret lathe made by Loudoun & McNab (Glasgow), the drills, a bending machine, which was basically a set of three rollers arranged in a pyramid with the top roller adjustable up or down through a worm gear to curve a straight piece of metal. This machine made the 'tyres' on the early farm carts and proved to be invaluable. Around 1970, it was converted to run with its own motor/reduction gearbox and today it is still used. Remarkably, the motor/gearbox combination also found a second life having been the drive off a Simplex dung dozer. This machine is still in regular use today, over 125 years later.

In the centre of the works there was the usual steel work benches each equipped with a vice. Next to them was a series of drilling machines and a reciprocating saw with a fifteen-

3.02 Irish carts without sides (top), with loose top sides (middle) and with harvest frames (bottom)

inch blade. The drawing office was not unlike a signal box, a wooden two-storey construction with glazed panels all around. The bottom half was a storeroom holding all the measuring equipment along with large drills and reamers, all jealously guarded by Gilmour Milton.

3.03 Gilmour Milton being promoted to Foreman at Pollocks, with Jimmy Black and Ronnie Campbell.

Over to the other half of the building were the cartwrights and wheelwrights, again the power to the machines was by a shaft running along the length of the building and a series of belts driving the machines. The machines were a Wadkin planer/thicknesser machine, Wadkin saw, large wood drill and various types of routers. For the men who had worked at Cowgatehead, it must have been a pleasure to work in such a modern facility.

Jimmy Dunlop, Senior, worked with Pollocks all his working life and was tasked with preparing all the carts for exhibition, overseeing the painting and adding the scroll work to the carts.

In 1916, whilst the war was going on, A. & W. Pollock continued manufacturing and selling farm implements. Messrs A. & J. Howat (Whitehill, Cumnock) purchased the following:

Bisset Binder complete with three horse tree for £36 0s 0d.
Water Proof Cover for the same for £1 0s 0d.
100 cwt of Binder Twine £3 5s 0d.
One Pole Wheel at 12s 6d.
Rail Carriage paid to Skares Station, consigned: -
1 Binder in 7 Parts, 1 Water Proof Cover, 2 Bags of Twine and 1 Pole Wheel.

The company took the decision not to exhibit at Edinburgh in 1919 and Aberdeen in 1920. Instead, it plumped for the Smithfield Show in London, showcasing their new factory and a complete exhibition of their wares on 11 December 1919.

The Smithfield Show was host to Pollock's main exhibit - the 'Perfect' potato digger, with the same digger also on display in 1919 after the war. The 1921 report on Smithfield saw a mention of a new all-steel saw bench, cart with harvest ladders along with a tipping cart of southern English style. This report demonstrates that A. & W. Pollock were prepared to alter their standard cart designs to suit that of a local nature, another example being the carts for the Irish market.

Smithfield was a great attraction for A. & W. Pollock and yielded substantial business opportunity. It was the ideal place to promote the Pollock Perfect Potato Digger which proved to be the main attraction on their stand. It was important to exhibit with maximum effect and impact but once again in 1920, A. & W. Pollock missed the Highland Show.

New Products were in short supply at the 1921 Highland Show in Stirling. However, A. & W. Pollock unveiled their new all-steel saw bench complete with 27-inch blade, belts, pulleys and guards.

A. & W. Pollock's new style saw bench with all steel construction was the order of the day at the 1921 Show at Smithfield. The show also played host to their cart with harvest ladders and a tipping cart of southern English style.

For Pollock's return to the Highland Show in 1921, it is recorded that the firm had an interesting display of implements including cheese press, curd mill, Barford and Perkins swath turner and the Pollock 'Perfect' potato digger.

The 1922 Highland Show at Dumfries saw an unusually small stand of Pollock implements on stand number 109. This was probably due to stand number 110 being occupied by none other than Wm. Nicolson (Newark), who Pollock represented from 1883.

A similar stand was prepared for Smithfield for 1922, 1923 and in 1924, displaying a new line of Hunter crown hoes, drill, grubbers and crown drill cultivators. This information puzzled me as to why we would exhibit a new line in hoe grubbers and crown drill cultivators all attributed to Hunters

3.04 Advertisement for Lister Engines, sold by Pollock.

of Maybole. More research was required and I found in the 1921 Census that the business premises of Hunter of Maybole had been taken over by A. Jack & Company (Maybole). So one can assume that probably after World War 1, T. Hunter ceased trading. Our leaflets for the early twenties show categorically show that although Hunter had gone, he would not be forgotten. A. & W. Pollock used the Hunter name for many years, as did A. Jack & Company. Many of Hunter's better known products, such as mangold sowers, are still seen today at vintage rallies. This was the format for shows in 1924-1927 with farm carts and tipping carts the focus for 1928-1929.

This information beggars the question if Pollocks, Jacks & Hunters had been working together. Was this another source of the many castings which were used by Pollocks? No evidence can be found, but it is certainly a possibility.

In 1923 A. & W. Pollock did not exhibit at the Highland in Inverness. By the time the show reached Perth in 1924, A. & W. Pollock only had a hand powered rick lifter, a refrigerator for milk and a cake breaker. Later that year, on 31 October 1924, T. & J. McErvel were offering Ransomes Powell and Pollock potato diggers, suggesting clean and easy potato digging is guaranteed if you use these diggers.

For the 1925 show in Glasgow, Pollock was offering Shank's patent water bowls as well as Lister refrigerators and barrel churns. Back to the Borders for the Highland Show of 1926 with A. & W. Pollock's Stand Number 117, next door to the Scottish Ford Dealers Association with such names as George and Jobling (Glasgow), Henry Alexander & Co Ltd (Edinburgh), Gale & Barclay Ltd (Glasgow), William Gillespie (Paisley), Fred Thomson (Dunfermline), Thomas Fairgrieve & Son and Stow & Harper Motor Co.

The Fordson Tractor of 1917 had been superseded by their 1926 water washer model and now were offering a variety of tractors, motor cars and a lorry conversion including:

Fordson Tractor with Agricultural Wheels
Fordson Tractor with Golf Course Wheels.
Fordson Tractor with Haulage Wheels
A 1 Ton Fordson Truck
Ford Touring Car
Ford 2 Seater – Lorry Conversion
Ford Sedan
Lincoln Motor Car

The tractors and cars that Ford were exhibiting were situated between the Pollock Stand and Bissets of Blairgowrie.

At Ayr Show in the open ground on the north side of the main roadway, Messrs A. & W. Pollock had on display, at Stand No. 26, a comprehensive selection of farming and dairy implements, in addition to a full range of drills, hoes and grubbers, discs, scarifiers and cultivators, all manufactured by the firm. There were many excellent designs of larger implements such as potato diggers, rollers, reapers and horse rakes; Albion and Bisset harvesting machinery, cattle drinking bowls, Lister churns, grinding mills and several designs of Lister oil and petrol engines were other features in this useful display.

3.05 Saw Bench, 1920.

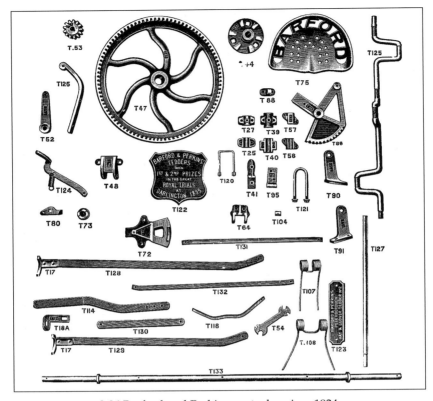

3.06 Barford and Perkins parts drawing, 1924.

The year 1927 saw another shift in the Pollock implement armoury. At the Highland Show, A. & W. Pollock had decided that their Pollock 'Perfect' potato digger, which had served the company so well for fifteen years, be superseded by their new 'Ideal' digger. It was agreed to continue to run the 'Perfect' as well. The 'Ideal' machine worked on a similar principle to the 'Perfect', but instead of wooden shafts to adjust the angle of the digging forks, A. & W. Pollock had designed a much simpler cam type arrangement. Therefore, the Pollock's 'Perfect' diggers, which were first introduced in 1909, had more or less reached the end of the road. However, both diggers were still on sale until 1950 when the 'Ideal' was dropped in favour of the 'Perfect' digger.

Barford & Perkins announced that they would be ceasing production of their farm implement business and concentrating on road roller production. The Barford & Perkins no. 2 hay tedder, which had been sold all over Scotland since 1913 by Pollocks, had now become surplus to Barford & Perkins due partly to the success of their road rollers, cricket pitch rollers and petrol engine road rollers.

Never one to miss an opportunity, Andrew and William Pollock saw this as an excellent new venture and purchased the sole manufacturing rights to the no. 2 tedder from Barford & Perkins. The basic machine was unchanged, all castings were badged Barford & Perkins and the only visible change was that of the wheels. The casting in the central hub now read Pollock (Mauchline) and the operator's seat on the later models was that of 'Pollock' extraction.

At the following season's Ayr Show in 1928, A. & W. Pollock were situated on Stand No. 25. The North British Agricultural reported that the stand was one of the largest and most comprehensive selection of up to date farming implements ever shown. Amongst the numerous exhibits were:

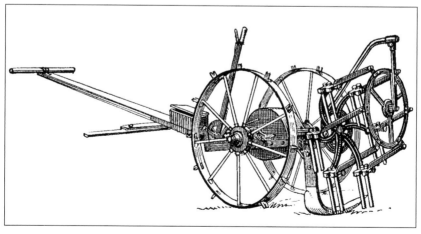

3.07 Ideal Potato Digger, c. 1928.

Martin's cultivators
Pollock disc harrow
Cleaner-milk steam
Sterilising system outfit for Grade 'A' milk which
claimed the attention of many dairy farmers.

Giving the Highland Show in Inverness in 1928 a miss was a disappointment for the many customer and friends. Having shown at Ayr six weeks earlier, the management felt that the long journey to Inverness was impractical merely due to distance. It should be noted that 'Pollocks of Mauchline' have supported the Highland Show and in fact have only missed fourteen shows excepting in the war years - 1914-1918 and 1940-1947. Most of these were in Inverness and Aberdeen.

Normal service was resumed for the Highland Show in 1929 at Alloa. The stand was on similar lines to previous shows with plenty of grubbers, scarifiers and ridgers as well as the Ideal potato digger. Included of course were the usual farm carts and rick lifters.

Over to Dumfries for 1930, a large forty-feet wide stand with no new implements on show held two rick lifters, one of the geared pattern and one hand powered.

Andrew and William recognised expansion and the need to look further afield than Scotland and in 1931, Pollock were exhibiting at Antrim, Ballymena and Newtonards shows on behalf of their agents T. & J. McErvel.

The 1931 show in Edinburgh saw Pollocks take their largest stand to date with sixty feet of space to be filled. It must have been quite a display as many implements were on show including:

Three different rick lifters
Pollock hay collector
Barford Perkins tedder
No. A4 and no. B4 carts with harvest frames
Sack lifter
Sack barrows
Byre barrows
Three types of Hunter hoes
No. 1, 2 & 3 cultivator
Ideal potato digger
Fodder barrow
Food cooler
Saw bench with twenty-four inch blade
Mower & reaper (Albion)
The first mention of a reaper from A. C. Bamlett
(Thirsk)
The 'Ideal' water bowl by Cruickshank's (Denny)

It is clear today why the Pollock Family were so well respected. Outstanding business men in their own rights, the Pollocks always looked out for others of a similar standing, looking for ways to improve working relationships and enhancing opportunities for show implements.

One such time came prior to the Inverness show in 1932, when the Highland Agricultural Show Society received a letter from Andrew Pollock suggesting that the show society would be doing a real service to the exhibitors if they arranged to have the rough grass round the stands cut before the arrival of any implements. It was remitted to the Stewards of the implements as well as the Engineers to decide to comply as far as possible with the request.

So, respected by members and management, Andrew Pollock had been made an Extraordinary Director of the Show. The newspapers at the time also reported that every prospect of Inverness Highland records had been broken.

The article in the 1932 'Review', covering the Smithfield Show of that year, states:

> That due to unprecedented demand for exhibition space, the stand size was restricted so no other exhibits, such as the Tedders formerly built by Barford and Perkins were on show.

At Smithfield in 1933, great play was made of the revolutionary farm carts with pneumatic tyres which were now available.

The Highland Show in 1934 heralded an innovation in farm carts, with the introduction of cart no. B4, fitted with coup body and Dunlop land wheels, to complement what was now becoming a large display of implements. It is very interesting to note that on an adjoining stand was Melotte separator sales, offering their French-built cream separator, with a fifty gallon per hour separator offered at £14 3s 6d. This French company was later represented by Gasgoine who made milking systems.

A new multi-purpose rick lifter, which can be a low side cart or flatbed rick lifter/hay bogie, with Dunlop pneumatic tyres was brought to market in 1934. This machine was awarded the Silver Medal in Belfast in 1935.

A. & W. Pollock continued to show at Smithfield up to 1939 when the war curtailed the show. The Smithfield Show became a must see for agriculturalists and farmers alike. William Pollock often spoke of meeting with the Bisset's of Blairgowrie who were great friends, William Elder of Berwick on Tweed, Alex Baird of Annan and Robert Weir of Strathaven, almost a who's who in implement-maker circles.

The War Office Campaign in 1939 heralded many companies to work together for the greater good. During this time, it was reported that the Americans provided many thousands of Fordson tractors for the war effort. There were also some Farmalls. The Pollock family never shied away from their war duties helping in many constructive ways including construction of much needed implements.

Aberdeen was the next port of call for A. & W. Pollock, with an all new rick lifter which was entered in the new implement section. This machine was a combined rick lifter and low loading transporter and as such was put forward for the Silver Medal which had alluded Pollocks since 1875. No award was made; however, a First Medal was presented at the Ulster Show for this implement which combined pneumatic tyres and side capes for cattle.

At Smithfield show on 7 December 1934, it was reported:

Scotland would be well represented at the Annual Dinner of R. A. Lister & Co Ltd, (Dursley, Gloucester) which takes place at the Café Royal, London. During the week of the fat stock show at Smithfield, Mr Waller Elliot MP is to be the Guest of Honour at this most prestigious dinner. The guest list reads like a who's who in the implement trade north of the border with such names as:
J. S. Henderson (Edinburgh)
T. Huchinson (Aberdeen)
Alex Baird (Annan)
Robert W. Weir (Strathaven)
William & John Elder (Berwick Upon Tweed)
William & Henry Rutherford (Berwickshire)
Andrew Pollock (Mauchline).

William Pollock by this time was married and had a son Andrew, followed in 1936 by John Reid Pollock – the next generation of implement makers was born.

As the years have passed, like many other shows, the Highland Show had grown. In 1935 at Aberdeen, Pollock's next-door neighbours at the show were A. Newlands & Son (Linlithgow) who had a fifty-foot stand offering a variety of wares including:

>
> Chain harrows (Wm Aitkenhead) £6 10s 6d
> Potato diggers (Blackstone) £26 0s 0d
> Bamford mower £26 5s 0d
> Mower (McCormick) £26 0s 0d
> Sowall grain drill (International Harvester Co)
> McCormick binder £56 0s 0d
> Farmall 12 tractor £160 0s 0d
> International manure distributor 9' 0" £22 10s 0d
>

Not to be outdone, Pollocks held their own and had an outstanding, albeit smaller, display showing the following pieces and various others of their own manufacture:

>
> Diamond harrows
> Disc harrows
> Two-furrow ploughs
> Perfect digger
>

In the following year, 1936, the Highland Show moved onto the border town of Melrose, where A. & W. Pollock were displaying a 12-disc single row harrow, six feet wide. This was the first year A. & W. had made a machine specifically for tractor use. Rick lifters now had a pole for tractor use and the farm carts were available with tractor poles and Dunlop pneumatic tyres. The rick lifters were fitted with Dunlop Special Pneumatic Wheels and Roller Bearing Axle. It was so designed that it could be instantly converted into a general purpose low loading float or cart, and thus it could be used throughout the whole year.

3.08 Letter and advert for Dunlop pneumatic tyres.

In 1937, the Highland Show was based at Alloa, a town previously visited in 1929. In the intervening eight years, however, agriculture was moving forward at a rapid pace. Most implements were being converted so that they were tractor-drawn as opposed to pulled by a horse.

The years between 1932-1937 had been very busy in Ireland but things were changing. Previous reports in the Irish press had always listed T. & J. McErvel, as sole agent for Ireland for A. & W. Pollock, but now there was competition as other companies came out of the woodwork to make their mark on the implement trade including:

Ransomes (Ipswich)
Pierce (Wexford)
R. & A. Lister (Dursley)
Blackstone & Co (Stamford)
Harrison, McGregor & Co (Leigh)

The Centenary Show of the Ayrshire Agriculture Society was held in 1937 with a record attendance and drawings over the two days of the show. It was to remain the largest in the history of the association. The presence of their Highnesses, the Duke and Duchess of Gloucester, created the utmost interest and enthusiasm. The figures for the two days showed an increase of £712 over those of the last year.

The Highland Show made its next visit to Dumfries in 1938 and because of its proximity to Mauchline, a large stand was the order of the day with no fewer than twenty-seven different implements on show, ranging from the Barford & Perkins tedder to the recently added disc harrows for both tractor and horse, and of course the old favourite 'Perfect' potato digger.

The Highland Show amongst others are great platforms to recognise hard work and excellence and the 1938 show in Ayr was no exception issuing a new implement award to A. Jack & Co, Maybole, for their Triplex machine for distributing fertiliser direct into the drill. As the name suggests, this machine covered three drills at once. A. & W. Pollock once again had a large display of implements with the only new machine being a single-row two-gang disc harrow for both horse and tractor.

Edinburgh was the venue for the 1939 Highland Show in late June which was to be the last show for eight years. Pollock's last stand for eight years was one of the biggest A. & W. Pollock had ever exhibited:

3.09 Rick Lifter with pneumatic tyres, c. 1935.

Three types of rick lifter, one with wrought iron steel wheels, one with pneumatic land wheels and shafts for horse and one with pole and hitch for tractor use.

The diameter of the blade on the saw bench had dropped from twenty-seven inch to twenty-four inch.

New improved farm carts which had all received pneumatic land wheels and roller baring axles.

Three types of Hunter hoe

Number 1, 2 and 3 grubbers

Pollock's Ideal digger

Barford and Perkins hay tedder complete with wind guard

Disc harrows for tractor

Food cooler

Food barrow

Fodder barrow.

# CHAPTER FOUR

# 1939-1981 Andrew & William Pollock (II)

The outbreak of war meant that Pollock's business had to adapt to war-time restrictions and lack of manpower, due to most men of working age being called up to take part in the hostilities.

In 1939, Ian Bryan, who had been an administration clerk for A. & W. Pollock since 1930, was called up to serve with the RAF during the war. After initial training in England, he was posted to Brindisi in Italy, Morocco and Algiers. On his demob, he was told to start back at the factory on the same terms as he left some five years earlier. An early part of his duties was to collect rent money from the Pollock owned properties in Mauchline which in 1916, totalled over twenty.

During this time, A. & W. Pollock did their bit for the war effort by building grubbers, harrows and disc harrows, all to assist the efforts of those fighting the war. It must be remembered that steel was in short supply and was allocated purely on a needs basis.

Eight years on from the last time the Highland Show had been held, the 1948 show was scheduled for Inverness and the 1949 show to be held in Dundee. A. & W. Pollock decided not to exhibit at either show, waiting for Paisley in 1950, where they exhibited a new trailer with detachable sides and brakes, swath turner (Albion) and a tractor-mounted reaper by A. C. Bamlett (Thirsk) plus their usual collection of implements.

Throughout the years, the Pollock Perfect digger sold well, nowhere better than in the Channel Islands. The Jersey famers were amazed at its lightness in draught and the ease with which the horses pulled this implement. A few were also sold in Guernsey.

For the Highland Show stand of 1950, at Paisley, Pollock exhibited a tractor trailer with detachable sides and brakes, the usual horse, hoe and grubbers, Ideal potato digger, Bamlett reaper, Albion swath turner and the Don manure sower, which sowed seed twelve feet six inches wide and was on pneumatic wheels. The next door stand was William Begg & Sons (Tarbolton) showing their range of ploughs. With the Mather Dairy Utensil Company from Dumfries, two stands away.

The year 1951 saw some radical improvements in the 'Perfect' digger, with the addition of a tractor drawback and a rotary screen. This was a tremendous improvement to a machine designed in 1908, as it put the potatoes in a 'windrow' greatly assisting the howkers in gathering the potato crop.

By now, the Pollock stand was beginning to look dated and although new products were always being tried out, only a small proportion of these reached the market for one or the other reason. The year 1951 was to be the last year of farm carts with only the coup cart being shown. The company management took the decision that year to introduce another new product, namely the tandem disc harrow, twenty-four discs for six feet wide and twenty-eight discs for seven feet, made for the growing number of tractors that were appearing on farms at the time.

I earlier alluded to the reason for not exhibiting at Inverness and Aberdeen. The company also made the decision not to go to the 1952 and 1953 Highland Shows at Kelso and Alloa, respectively. It was in 1954 that Pollocks made a return to Dumfries for the season's Highland Show with two new trailers – one tipping and one fast body, as well as their normal display. It is very interesting to know that every single item on display was of their own manufacture.

The show in Dumfries saw the popular rick lifter with attachments to suit hydraulic lift or tractor. Also on show were two types of farm trailers and forward controls as well as the Perfect potato digger, but Pollock were still offering horse implements, the Hunter crown hoe and drill grubbers.

The following year, 1955, took A. & W. Pollock to Edinburgh. On the Edinburgh stand, the firm displayed an almost identical stand to the previous year, except for the Pollock all-steel saw bench, which by this time had acquired a three-point linkage for transporting it.

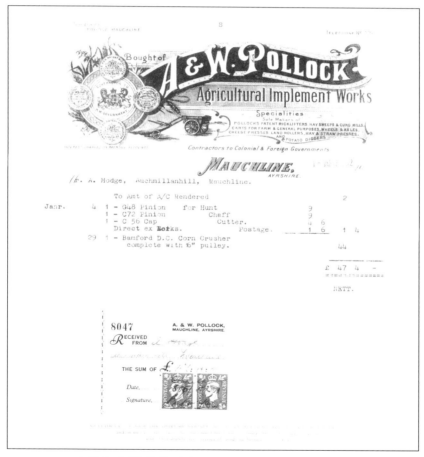

4.01 A. & W. Pollock letterhead with bill from 1952.

The 1956 Highland Show in Inverness was avoided by A. & W. Pollock, but the company returned to the 'Highland' in 1957 for the exhibition in Dundee. There, Pollocks exhibited the Barford and Perkins tedder with forward controls and a drawbar for tractor use, a new haysweep, both folding and hydraulic lift, and their tandem disc harrows with transport wheels available in both six-foot and seven-foot wide variations, also with eighteen inch and twenty-inch diameter discs. These tandems disc harrows sold in large numbers and were manufactured up until 1970.

In 1958, John Pollock, who for the previous five years was a management trainee with Blackstone of Stamford, came back to Mauchline to take up a position with the company. Blackstone were the leading manufacturers of farm implements. They also operated their own foundry, heavy and light machine shops, and generated their own power. This was truly an ideal place to learn the various processes required to build implements. A. & W. Pollock converted to a Limited Company in 1958.

John did not take long to adjust and by 1959, the Barford & Perkins Hay tedder, built by Pollock since around 1925, was exhibited at the Royal Highland Agricultural Show, complete with power drive instead of land drive. Several prototypes were built and exhaustively tested throughout Ayrshire, Dumfriesshire and Galloway, but it was found that the increase in speed and horse power proved problematic and the prototypes were abandoned.

It is always good to be close to home and the 1958 Highland gave the company just that with a return to home territory. The Ayrshire Agricultural Show Ground in Ayr was the venue. All around the stand was modern farm equipment from other companies such as:

# Apprenticeship Agreement

This Apprenticeship Agreement is entered into between __A.& W., Pollock Ltd.__ of __Mauchline, Ayrshire.__ (hereinafter called "The Employer") and __James McGhee__ of __Cumnock__ (hereinafter called "the Apprentice") whose date of birth is the __fifteenth__ day of __July__ 19 __51__, with the consent of __David McGhee__ of __Cumnock__ (hereinafter called the *" Parent/Guardian ") as follows :—

1. The **Employer** agrees to accept the **Apprentice** as an __agricultural engineering__ apprentice as from __14th August, 1967__, and to carry out the obligations in and train him in accordance with the Scheme of Recruitment and Training agreed by the Scottish Agricultural Machinery Apprenticeship Training Committee.

2. The *Parent/Guardian and the **Apprentice** jointly and severally agree to carry out the terms of the Scheme of Recruitment and Training agreed by the Scottish Agricultural Machinery Apprenticeship Training Committee.

In Witness Whereof these presents are subscribed by the parties hereto on the __14th__ day of __August__ 19 __67__, as follows :—

Witness

Address __22 Lonhill Ave Lanark__

Occupation __Director.__

Witness __Geo McKinnon__

Address __58 Beechwood Road Mauchline__

Occupation __DRAUGHTSMAN__

For A. & W. POLLOCK, LTD.

Director.

Employer

X James McGhee
Apprentice

X David McGhee
*Parent/Guardian

* Delete whichever is not applicable.

## CERTIFICATE OF COMPLETION OF APPRENTICESHIP

The Agreement of Apprenticeship having been faithfully completed to the satisfaction of the Training Employer and the Joint Apprenticeship and Training Committee of the Scottish Agricultural Machinery Industry is hereby endorsed the __fourteenth__ day of __August__ 19 __71__.

Chairman of the Joint Apprenticeship and Training Committee.

A. & W. POLLOCK LTD.
MAUCHLINE
Tel. 221. Address of the Training AYRSHIRE.

4.02 Jimmy McGhee's Apprenticeship Agreement 1951

Bamfords, with a display of pick-up balers, mowers, manure spreaders and oat crushers.

Jones balers with their mk. II baler with engine of twenty horse power.

Armstrong-Siddeley, new 'Pilot' combined harvester, complete with David Brown Petrol/Paraffin engine, and their double action tedder with power drive.

Right next door to Pollock's stand was Stewart Plant Ltd, displaying JCBs, Hydra Digga, Marshall Crawler and a selection of pumps and generators which they have now become major suppliers for.

On to the Pollock stand which held a large display of mainly their own build with a sprinkling of their main agencies represented such as Lister-Blackstone Elevators, Albion Swath Turner, Vicon-Lelys Acrobat, Wolley's Steam Sterilising Plant and a Bamlet Reaper. Their new machine was the Pollock 'Perfect' Digger which by now was mounted on a three-point linkage and had acquired a power drive. Along with this on the stand was their Hay Sweep, folding and power, lift and non-folding. This show was the last time the Highland would ever visit Ayr as in 1960, the show settled in Edinburgh and has been at Ingliston ever since.

The 1958 Ayr show had horse implements on display for sale but, due to the decline of horses in favour of tractors, these implements were now deemed obsolete. As well as moving to a new purpose built showground on the outskirts of Edinburgh, the 'Highland' as the show had been known, became the Royal Highland Show in 1960.

A. & W. Pollock had but one more trip to make - to Aberdeen in 1959 for the Highland's final visit as a travelling show.

4.03 Pollock's Potato Digger being used at Broomfield, Cumnock, around 1940.

At the 1960 Highland Show, every item on display was for tractor operation with a power drive hay tedder, a wheel drive hay tedder, seven-foot disc harrow, mounted drill hoe, triple crown mounted drill hoe with discs - triple mounted. The purpose of the stand was to show the future of farming with tractors instead of horses. Once John Pollock had returned to the company, his impact on the future of the business was felt almost immediately with a power drive hay tedder entered in the new implement category at the 1960 Highland Show.

The next-door neighbours on that occasion was Salopian Kenneth Hudson and Son (Whitchurch in Salop), showing their PZ quick hay maker, swath turner and tedder, the Warnock land leveller and clod breaker and heavy duty cultivator and broadcaster fertiliser and distributor.

Around 1960, John and his father attended many sales at O. D. D. Bowhouse where the government were disposing of a large number of trucks and machine tools which were used in the manufacture of ordnance. What was on offer certainly did not disappoint the Pollocks. They purchased a radial drill and a Herbert No. 5 S.E. turret lathe to augment the Loudoun and McNab turret lathe which by the 1960s was getting very long in the tooth.

The year 1960 was also to be a defining year in the history of Pollocks as Andrew, older brother of William Pollock died on 3 January age 72. This left father and son at the implement works on their own. Undeterred by this, John heard about a group of young farmers going on a trip to America's dairy county and along with Malcolm Logan (Kirkland's) and Walter Hogarth (Knockrivoch, Ardrossan), John secured his place on what was to become a very fruitful visit to the USA.

Settling in America for this short business trip, they were taken to some of the very large dairy units which featured some of the first tower silos and the ancillary feeding systems and scraping systems. Colman and Company who were agents for the tower silos arranged this trip. John was very impressed but felt the UK was not ready for such revolutionary equipment as blowers, unloaders and belt feeders all working in conjunction with tower silos. However, the cow sheds with their narrow gutters and scraper system impressed him greatly and buoyed up, he could not wait to get back to his father to explain what he had seen in America.

John proved to be a welcome asset and a driving force in the business and by 1961, the company was offering two-row precision seeders, two-row mounted disc drill scarifiers, combined seeder/scarifiers, hay tedder wheel drive, mounted disc harrows and nest boxes, brooder boxes, sack barrows and sack lifters. Also of note was Pollock's next door neighbour on that occasion, who were none other than New Holland Machine Company Ltd

**A. & W. POLLOCK**

*Agricultural Implement Works*

MAUCHLINE

*Specialities—*

POLLOCK'S PATENT RICKLIFTERS
HAY SWEEPS AND CURD MILLS
CARTS FOR FARM AND GENERAL PURPOSES
WHEELS AND AXLES
CHEESE PRESSES
LAND ROLLERS
POTATO DIGGERS, ETC.

*Contractors to*

COLONIAL AND FOREIGN GOVERNMENTS

———

*Telegrams :*                              *Telephone :*
" POLLOCK, MAUCHLINE."    MAUCHLINE 221

4.04 Advertisement from 1953 Mauchline Coronation Celebrations.

showing their latest Super Hayliner 68, Super Hayline 78, Crop Chopper 33, Crimper 401-5, Forage Box - Model 300 and Crop Carrier No. 3.

At that time, Pollock had its usual display of solely Pollock-manufactured products on show, largely because most of its long-held agencies were now exhibiting. On show was Polloxk's new tedder, introduced in 1959 along with its mounted disc harrows, triple crown mounted grubber and a large collection of nest boxes, brooder boxes, stable barrows and meal barrows.

During this time, many other ideas were being born and it suggested that the boxes were a stop gap as John Pollock worked on these projects which were due to be unveiled at Ayr and the Royal Highland Show in 1963.

At Ingliston in 1962, three new products were shown for the first time – two-row ridge mounted disc drill scarifiers, two ridge mounted precision seeders and a combined seeder/scarifiers built into the same frame. At the same show, New Holland were showing their '33' Double Chop, '30' Flail Mower and their super '68' Hayliner Hay Baler.

In the same year, Pollock's stand was next door neighbours to Charles J. Marshall, who were exhibiting their new range of trailers. One of these was fitted with grain sides, one with silage sides and a trailer with bale extensions. Silage making in the late fifties and early sixties was gaining in popularity with our near neighbours at the show all devoting some stand space to these types of implements.

After a fruitful and busy year, 1962 gave A. & W. Pollock the opportunity to show a new electric drive rotary turnip cutter, two ridge precision drill, two row mounted disc drill/scarifiers, combined seeder/scarifiers, triple crown mounted hoe with grubber tines scarifying plates and discs, wheel drive hay tedder, mounted discs and trailer discs.

John was a great researcher and looked at many implements already in use including the byre cleaning systems which had been manufactured in the UK, but mainly consisted of conveyor belt laid the length of the byre which fed the cow muck direct to the dung stead. Dickies (East Kilbride), made a reasonably good system and Simplex also made their dung dozer which was totally different as it used a reduction gearbox linked to a track and reciprocated back and forth. Neither of their options suited John as he had seen various round the shed cleaners with elevators to discharge the cow muck into a spreader or pile it into a dung heap.

The company had been working on a new prototype and in 1962, the Pollock byre cleaner system was fully operational and ready to be rolled out. By September 1963, the works manager, Gilmour Milton, and head welder fabrication, Jimmy Thomson, installed and commissioned byre cleaner number 2 at Kilmaurs Mains for Mr J. Smith. Machine number 1 is listed as being the Royal Highland Show exhibit.

On to 1963, and our next byre cleaner went south of the border to Mr W. Edgar (Burthwaite Hill, Wreay, Carlisle), sold by Joseph Hillary of Aspatria. Orders were coming in thick and fast for this revolutionary system. Dairy, pig, poultry and beef farmers all tried out the Pollock byre cleaner system. The first system in a pig unit went to H. Robertson & Son (Laurencekirk), being Number 10, with Number 12 sold to Messrs Mason (Omoa), the well-known knackers and slaughterhouse operators in Newarthill, Lanarkshire.

Lawsons of Dyce were a well-known maker of sausage and curers of ham. They purchased machine Number 27. By now, the list of agents wanting to sell the byre cleaner was rapidly increasing so much that within the first 150 machines, the following firms all sold byre cleaners:

4.05 Pollock's Byre Cleaner, in operation 1963.

Oliver & Snowden (Carlisle)
Farm Mechanisation (Cupar, Fife)
Joseph Hillary of Aspatria (West Cumberland)
Barclay Ross & Hutchinson (Aberdeen)
Rickerby Ltd (Currock Road, Carlisle)
R. Howie & Sons (Parkhead, Dunlop)
W. Elder (Berwick Upon Tweed)
Kintyre Farmers (Campbeltown)
Robert B. Massey (Market Weighton)
C. & M. Hesford (Ormskirk, Lancashire)
Charles Weir (Strathaven)
H. Pigney & Sons (Appleby, Westmorland)

West Cumberland Farmers (Penrith)
James Jack, (Hyndford) Ltd (Lanark)
McCaskies Farm Supplies (Stirling)
Associated Agricultural Oils (Millhall, Stirling)
Beacon Trailers (Penrith)
Mather & Co Dairy Utensils (Terregles Street, Dumfries)
Youngs Ltd (Chester Le Street, Durham)

As can be seen, from this list, the agents were spread far and wide. However, the number of agents who sold large numbers of machines were Barclay Ross & Hutchison, Joseph Hillary, Rickerby Ltd, James Jack (Hyndford) Ltd, Mather & Co (Dumfries) and Kintyre Farmers. Pollocks tended to give these agents a complete area and pretty much were sole agents for that area.

A. & W. Pollock's line up for 1963 Ayr & Highland shows looked very modern, offering precision seeders, mounted drill scarifiers, combined seed-scarifier, triple crown mounted hoe, hay tedder, mounted tandem disc harrows, trailed disc harrows and byre cleaners, but by now the competition was fierce. Many of the old established companies, especially implement makers, would fail in the coming years. However, the 1963 show will be remembered for the introduction of the Pollock byre cleaner to the general public. Little did John Pollock know this 'Mucker' as it was known locally, would provide employment for his loyal staff for many years to come.

The New Holland Agency was well sought after and was held by A. Jack & Sons (Maybole) who had been trading for well over a century but ceased trading around 1964. This range offered mowers, hay turners, balers, flail mowers, double chop forage harvester and precision chop forage harvesters, all of which were in demand in the 60's and 70's.

Along with this agency, came John McCulloch, a native of Maybole, and long term employee of Jacks. John's father was a highly-regarded provost of Maybole and John himself was a well-known and well respected agriculturalist.

As the years rolled on so did our ability to produce more A. & W. Pollock manufactured equipment. Our 1964 stand only contained machinery manufactured by A. & W. Pollock Ltd, although severely curtailed due to the success of the byre cleaner, with only Pollock buckrakes and eight-, ten-, and twelve-tine models. The two-row scarifiers and the two-row seed drill surviving the rationalising of products.

4.06 Byre Cleaner elevator of around 1964.

In 1964, we were next to J. Bisset & Sons, Morris Motors, Martin Markham, John D. Allen and the Ayrshire Elevator Co. Alas, A. & W. Pollock Ltd, are the only survivors still trading.

By December 1965, Pollock had reached byre cleaner number 75 and the following year we had sold one hundred and fifty byre cleaners.

Machine Number 96 was sold to Whessoeville Farms (Darlington) as a forage feeder in a narrow shed which formerly housed a belt feeder from a forage tower, a system not favoured by John Pollock. The number of agents now selling byre cleaners meant that the production of the machines that had supported Pollock for the last fifty years would have to be rationalised, and many of the machines by 1966 had been deleted from their range. So much so that the only survivors were – mounted disc harrows, scarifiers and buck rakes. In addition, the firm sold carryover stocks of Pollock's Perfect potato digger, the Barford & Perkins tedder and sack barrows until stocks were exhausted.

For 1965 A. & W. Pollock Ltd showed all their current products, Buckrakes, Disc Harrows and Row Scarifiers, Two-Row Seed Drill, Combined Seeder and Ripple Hoes. The 1965 'Highland' was to be the last of implements made for almost a century as from 1966 onwards, the stand was dedicated to byre cleaners alone.

4.07 Ayr Show stand in 1966

4.08 Pollock's stand at the Highland Show, approximately 1964.

In 1966, at the Royal Highland Agricultural Show, John Pollock was provided with a very rare opportunity. Mr Y. Hayashi of Cornes & Co, came on to the stand and queried John on the prospect of providing a machine for test and evaluation purposes. This plan was approved in Tokyo and an order was sent to the implement works and despatched 4 August 1966. Things were going well and the machine dispatched proved itself on the farm where it was installed.

Everything was ticking over nicely, sales of balers were going well with one season alone reaping the sale of some twenty-six. Forage harvesters were gaining a large foothold in the market place and other machines such as mowers, tedders and combine harvesters were also being sold. All in all, the late 60s and early 70s could have been described as a purple patch in the company's history.

With byre cleaners now selling extremely well, John Pollock set about building a proper display unit for byre cleaners. This unit comprised of a gable end of a byre with an elevator protruding out and a dung spreader below, along

93

with a collection of pictures showing all the different layouts possible.

John Pollock had been aware for some time that the age profile of his employees was probably fifty-plus, and with a new product well underway, recruitment was necessary. Gilmour Milton, Works Foreman, was by now 68 years' old and was instrumental in finding his replacement in David Goudie. He was a well-known local man who lived in West Park Avenue, only a stone's throw from the implement works. This was undoubtedly one of John Pollock's finest decisions. Davy, prior to joining A. & W. Pollock Ltd, had spent the war years in Germany with the Royal Electrical and Mechanical Engineers, gathering disabled tanks and all other kinds of ordinance.

Davy was an inspector in the lens department at the optical works at the Haugh, where an industrial dispute took place which was well documented both locally and nationally. After this dispute was settled many optical factory employees sought new employment. Davy left for a Government training position in engineering. On hearing this, Gilmour Milton suggested there may well be an opening at A. & W. Pollock's.

Davy contacted John Pollock, who was impressed with his enthusiasm and his knowledge of farming, and immediately offered him a job starting in January of the following year (1967).

John Pollock, since starting with the business in 1958, had employed apprentice engineers with Hugh Nimmo, Louis McPhillips, Tom Dunlop, Bobby Collins, John Weir, John Price and myself all starting within a three-year time frame, joining with recently qualified tradesmen, William Monaghan, Eddie McMurdo and John Blakely (who later emigrated to Australia).

Tom Dunlop, John Weir and myself are still involved in agriculture, with Tom having left for Agricultural Central

Trading (A. C. T.) then to Taskers of Andover, settling with Kubota for the last thirty odd years. John Weir also went to A. C. T. before joining E. T. C. Mill Loaders, then to Andrew Alston & Son, Benston Smiddy, and the remainder being spent with Lloyds of Dumfries. John Price married Alison Possee from Thornhill and left Pollocks to work with Rickerby Ltd, our agents. He then went back home to his native Wales where he has remained ever since. John and I became great friends, a friendship which has lasted for almost fifty years and one which is treasured.

In August 1967, the Pollock fleet of vehicles included a Vauxhall 490 Estate, a Vauxhall 101 for John & his father a series II Land Rover PAG858, a BMC 3.5 Ton Truck (registration number CCS 13C) and two Bedford HA vans. By 1972 all had been replaced with John Pollock now driving a Vauxhall Ventora 3.3 litre estate, Bedford TK 3.5 Ton truck (registration number XCS 13K), a Ford Transit pick up, two Bedford HA vans, and salesman John McCulloch acquired a brand-new Austin Maxi.

The Ford transit was by far the most popular vehicle in the fleet for many of the men, none more so than Louis McPhillips. I remember being out at a job in Kilmaurs with Louis. Unbeknown to me, he had adjusted the window washers to point to the left and right of the vehicle, and on passing a traffic warden or member of the public he would depress the foot pump and soak anyone who would happen to be passing! Ah, those were the days!

John Pollock had a rather strange collection of vehicles throughout his working life. Along with the aforementioned vehicles, John also had a Citroen Safari D Special, Talbot Tagora, Daimler/Jaguar, MGB GT, Ford Capri 3-litre, and Citroen BX 1.9D - all in all ,an offbeat collection.

The starting rate for apprentices in 1967 was two shillings and a halfpenny an hour, or £4 1s 8d for a forty-hour week,

4.09 Bobby Collins in Pollock's 'Big Factory', c. 1967.

with a deduction of five shillings for National Insurance. My nett take home pay was £3 16s 8d, with second year apprentices receiving £5 16s 8d. My mother often remarked how little was left after paying my ten-journey bus fare, 12s 0d, and pocket money of 10s. The wage for a journeyman at the time was £14 10s 0d per week.

Behind the scenes, there were many good people who kept the business going and in 1967, these included the office staff comprising of Ian Bryan, Margaret Smith, William Pollock and John Pollock. Margaret was a Netherthird girl, living just two hundred yards from my mother and father. Her father was a miner and a staunch trade unionist, fairly similar to my own father. Margaret was going steady with Cumnock man Joe Stillie and they were due to be married. With the business buoyant with Japanese orders, her young sister Jacqueline joined her in the office. Around 1970, Margaret left to start a family.

In 1973 the Stillies had a son, Derek, who had become a household name as a Scotland Under-21 international goal keeper. He also played for Aberdeen, Dunfermline and a few English league teams.

In August 1971, Jean Watson of Muirston farm started as a clerical assistant. Jean was a very fashion-conscious girl, wearing all modern clothes but especially her miniskirts. This did not go unnoticed in the factory, with a fair number of apprentices' eyes popping out of their head at this amazing sight!

Another apprentice was Jim Richmond of Dykefield farm, Mauchline, who served his apprenticeship along with Michael Wood, Alex Kirkwood, Kenny Fowler and John Sharp. He left in 1981 to work with Jim Mair, Contractor, and on to the well-known business of J. H. McNae of Tarbolton, where he has remained ever since. It is remarkable nowadays for employees to stay in the same job for twenty-five years, never mind fifty, but A. & W. Pollock can hold its head high in this regard.

Sales in the UK continued to be good. However, 4 May 1967 proved to be a Red-Letter Day as Cornes & Co ordered the first shipment of ten byre cleaner units for Japan. These units were dispatched in record time and were heading for Yokohama by 29 Aug 1967.

4.10 Aerial photograph of implement works, Mauchline, June 1974.

Soon the pressures of exporting were beginning to tell and John Pollock called a meeting, the outcome of this was a bonus system that would be put into place. For every byre cleaner that was exported, we would be paid the sum of 27s 6d, pro rata for apprentices. This scheme worked well and I do not remember missing a deadline for shipping.

The units built at Mauchline were all fabricated to a standard Japanese specification which comprised of:

1 sixteen-foot elevator complete with return side
1 transmission unit and cover
220 paddles compete with chain (approximately 100m)
3 corner idlers
1 reverse curve guide 90 degrees
1 baseplate complete with hold down shoes.

Many orders were received for incomplete systems as the Japanese method of ordering to a standard specification was flawed in as much as they only ordered standard units, but as we all know, no two farms are alike whether in Japan or Britain.

The only other detail we required was the rotation in which the chain and paddles would drive. In the early days of exporting, the complete order would be packed in crates, all tailor made from 1⅛ inch white pine tongue and groove flooring – all best quality. With former cartwrights still on the workforce, namely Jimmy Dunlop and Bobby Hair, they were now fully employed at their chosen trade. Jimmy's father, James Dunlop (Senior), worked at A. & W. Pollock all his working life. Young Jimmy had served his apprenticeship at Pollocks, but left for the Mauchline Quarries, only to return for the rest of his working life at the firm.

Many more orders were to follow this shipment and dispatches are recorded for Kobe, Yokohama and Otaru in Japan between 1966-1976.

The first machine dispatched to the Land of the Rising Sun was logged as Machine Number 135 with the subsequent ten units being logged as Machine No's 208-217. It was a long wait for the next order from Japan. It was not placed until January 1968. For the initial dispatches, McKinnon Transport Haulage Contractors (Kilmarnock) took the machines to Southampton for loading onto ships of the NYK Lines, Nippon, Yusen Kaisha. All these ships had 'Maru' in their names - like Kamakura Maru which we used along with the Kitano Maru. All the shipping documents were handled by shipping agents in Glasgow, Gellatly Hankey & Co, who issued A. G. numbers and destinations.

Alex Houston of Cumnock was appointed as our logistics company and we would liaise on all shipping dates, expected sailings and when goods would be allowed for loading. The year 1968 was a better year all round with orders for 35 units being placed. As can be seen by the serial numbers, we reached 500 units sold. By December 1969, approximately 50% of these were home market and 50% were Japan.

Our overseas sales were not restricted to Japan as on 26 December 1967, we sold our first unit to Mr MacDonald of Auchamore on the Isle of Gigha, logged as Machine Number 260. September 18, 1969, saw us install the first 48 feet elevator in a pig unit for H. Pickervance, New Hay Pig Farm (near Kirkham). This was to be the first of many units to customers.

As often happens, there is always something lurking just around the corner. William Pollock was by now 82 and during the factory's annual holiday, in August 1971, he died, being survived by his wife and two sons, John and Andrew.

Much has been written about John but his brother Andrew chose another career path, that of a doctor. After studying under Professor Thomas Symington (a native of Muirkirk), Andrew studied haematology, then decided to seek a post in Birmingham Hospital, a position held for many years. A middle-aged man, Andrew left Birmingham for Hong Kong and thereafter at Kingston Royal in Jamaica and back to England to Addenbrooks Hospital in Cambridge.

## PRICE LIST

January, 1970

**ELEVATOR/TRANSMISSION UNIT**
including 16 ft. steel plate elevator with standard or tip-up paddles, elevator stand, transmission and cover, chain tensioner, baseplate, mounting box, and complete with electric motor and starter.

|  |  |  |  |
|---|---|---|---|
| 3 h.p., 3 phase | £250 | 0 | 0 |
| extra for 5 h.p., 3 phase | 5 | 0 | 0 |
| extra for 3 h.p., 1 phase | 25 | 0 | 0 |
| extra for 5 h.p., 1 phase | 35 | 0 | 0 |
| extra for each 2 ft. of elevator length required, over 16 ft. | 5 | 0 | 0 |
| allowance for each 2 ft. of elevator length not required, under 16 ft. | 5 | 0 | 0 |
| extra for high-torque transmission unit (large installations) | 50 | 0 | 0 |

**CHAIN**

| forged steel chain, complete with paddles at 18 in. spacing, **per foot** | 1 | 5 | 0 |
|---|---|---|---|

**CORNER FIXTURES**

| Standard 90° Corner Idler Wheel Assembly, each | 12 | 0 | 0 |
|---|---|---|---|
| Standard 90° Reverse Curve Chain Guide Assembly, each | 12 | 0 | 0 |
| Offsets and non-standard Fixtures, each | 12 | 0 | 0 |

**SLIDE RAILS**

| Gutter slide rails (supplied in 4 ft. sections) **per foot** | 0 | 3 | 0 |
|---|---|---|---|

(Moulds and Formers remain the property of A. & W. Pollock, Ltd., and are chargeable if not returned.)

* * * * * * * * * * * * * * * * * * * * * * * * * * * * * * * * * * * * * * * * * * * * * * * * * * * * * * * * * *

### NOTES.

All prices are EX WORKS.
All equipment is offered subject to the Company's Conditions of Sale.
All previous price lists cancelled.
Prices and specifications subject to alteration without notice.

## A. & W. POLLOCK, LTD.

### MAUCHLINE, AYRSHIRE

Telegrams: "POLLOCK, MAUCHLINE"     Telephones: MAUCHLINE 221 & 461

4.11 Byre Cleaner Price List from 1970

4.12 Gilmour Milton's retiral dinner, 1968. On left (seated with suit is William Pollock. Gilmour Milton standing. To right of him is Margaret Pollock and John R. Pollock.

From my own time with the firm, and the knowledge I have gleamed from the family, I discovered that in the early 1970s, John Pollock was preparing his grandfather's records, medals and patents for the Museum of Scottish Antiquities, in case this history was lost in the mist of time. While looking through the archive, he came across three sheets of gold leaf, which was used in special events carts, and paintbrushes with extra-long bristles which Jimmy Dunlop had used.

With the death of William Pollock in 1971, the last link to the nineteenth century was broken. Despite the surrounding sadness, it was to be business as usual for the Pollock family. However, as earlier mentioned, a long-serving employee, Gilmour Milton, worked for Pollocks for a lifetime of over 56 years. John M. Bryan from Catrine had also joined the company as a boy and worked for Pollocks all his working life except for the war years where he saw active service in Brindsi, Italy, Morocco and Algiers as well as various postings in England.

Between Christmas and New Year 1971, John invited all the employees to wait behind for a celebratory drink and buffet (a tray of pies from Young's the Bakers in Mauchline). We had a super time recounting stories and incidents in the past years. Full of alcohol, we set out for home via the Railway Hotel in Auchinleck, where much more alcohol was consumed. Bobby Collins, John Weir and myself were enjoying a drink when Collins suddenly tumbled off the bar stool and onto a table of drinks. The barman immediately left his position behind the bar, came round to Collins and put the boot in his ribs. On seeing this, I was offended and whacked the barman on the nose. In the ensuing struggle, the barman returned my compliment, John Weir at this time was being sick in the gents' toilet and struck the bridge of his nose with the toilet seat, resulting in black eyes for both of us and Bobby with sore ribs.

Our next escapade was at my stag party in March 1972 held in the Snug Bar in Cumnock. Having consumed copious amounts of alcohol, I then invited all the boys to my parents' home in Netherthird. By eleven o'clock that evening, the effects of the alcohol were telling on me and my mother suggested I should go to bed while my father arranged a minibus to take the rest of the lads home. Alex Stewart taxis of Cumnock was contacted by my father. He immediately refused to come and collect the party unless my father would accompany the less than sober crowd back to Mauchline.

In March 1972, I was married to a local girl, Effie Jamieson. Later that year, I was injured while playing football and ended up in hospital for surgery on a ruptured cartilage. Whilst recovering, I was called into the office. John Pollock announced he was looking for someone both literate and numerate, with an ability to interpret drawings and indeed produce drawings, and as he had precious few to choose from, I was the ideal candidate. Unsure whether I had been paid a compliment or not, John added that if, after a trial period of three months, I did not adjust to office work, or I was happier in the works, the position could be reversed. I readily agreed and the following Monday I was installed in my new position as Assistant Draughtsman and Clerk for the export paperwork required for Japanese orders. This proved to be a great opportunity for me and one which would change the path of my life for good.

George McKinnon had occupied the draughtsman position for a few years and would now go out to deal with enquiries, measure the cow sheds, calculate a quotation and provide me with the details required to produce a set of drawings for reach job. This continued for some time and on the sudden departure of Tom Dunlop, going to a competitor, A. C. T., the door was opened for me to go into the retail shop and stores.

John McCulloch came into the stores every morning along with Ian Bryan who would oversee all the purchase orders and stock orders required and John would process his orders to ensure we had stock to cover these.

4.13 Drawing of Pollock's byre cleaner.

Our despatches in 1972 were rather disappointing with only 47 units against the 75 units of the previous year. However, in 1973, things were going full tilt with 130 units on order. However, with the workload at home, some of them were not despatched until early 1974. The year 1974 itself was a bumper year with orders totalling 190 units. Each order was detailed with the specification and the port to which it was to be despatched and in what order they were expected.

By around January 1973 we had sold 1,000 units with machine No's 1001-1012 going to Kobe in Japan. It should be noted that research and development work was continuing at Mauchline and a deputation from Cornes and Co arrived at the factory in early 1970, to view our new type of galvanised elevators, as well as taking in some local installations including the Forage Feeder which was installed for G. Milroy and Sons, Fardenreoch farm (Pinwherry). This installation of a feed unit is still fully operational fifty years later, only requiring some new bearings, sprockets and chains, complete with paddles.

Farmers in Japan were beginning to look for something bespoke rather than a bog-standard installation and we designed a 24' swinging elevator for use on the more remote farm where snow was a problem in the winter. These units were logged as 941 and 942 on 18 July 1972. The feedback we received was positive and many more orders were to follow.

By the end of 1973, sales were very good in both manufacturing and retail. Prices were soaring out of control with inflation almost reaching an eye-watering 19%. Petrol costs were £0.38 per gallon rising to £0.49½. In 1974, a fuel crisis was well underway.

In January 1974, the then Government announced that from 1 January onwards, we would only have electricity three days a week. John Pollock acted right away, installing a 25kVa generator, kindly supplied by Jim Watson of Muirston, Jean's father.

4.14 Japanese leaflet issued by Cornes & Co. depicting Pollock machinery, c. 1968.

Jean remembers well her father's reaction to the extra money earned by supplying the tractor and generator. He bought each of his four daughters a piece of jewellery as a keepsake. Unfortunately, no mention was made of his son Willie or wife Jean receiving remuneration from this transaction but knowing Jim, I am sure they would have also been suitably rewarded.

Apparently, the three-day week was caused by the National Union of Mineworkers rejecting an offer of a 19% increase in wages and threating strike action.

The country was split 50/50 by this course of action. However, with my father, grandfather and great grandfather all having been coal miners, I certainly knew where my loyalty lay.

During the fuel crisis, our travel had been curtailed. Although we had a full order book from Japan, we still had to fulfil our commitments on the home front. One customer had purchased a byre cleaner two years previously and was

4.15 Lorry going to Japan, 1967.

waiting patiently for his second unit to be installed. We informed him that due to the shortage of diesel, we could come to Yorkshire, but we were unable to get enough diesel to come home. The farmer replied, get your men down here and I will guarantee you will get enough fuel to get home.

4.16 Mediaeval Banquet held at Adamton House Hotel, Prestwick, to entertain Japanese customers, c. 1969.

We installed the unit and were ready to go home, the farmer proceeded to fill our tank with red diesel commenting, 'I only promised enough fuel to take you home, the colour was not specified!'

In 1973 at hay time a call was received from a customer in the Kilmarnock area requiring a baler engineer to call. This particular baler, a New Holland Super Hayliner 268, was not in the same class as the baler it replaced, the N.H. Superliner 68, and had a nasty habit of producing 'banana'-shaped bales in very dense crops. The usual remedy was to adjust the feed packers. The 268 had six as opposed to the 68 which had only four. Bobby Collins attended the baler, worked at it for around an hour adjusting the feed packers and then said, 'Okay, farmer, round the field,' to test his work. By this time the sun was bearing down, the farmer's frustration growing by the minute. Why oh why is this baler producing banana shaped bales? 'It might just have something to do with the monkey on the tractor,' Collins replied, quick as a flash. The farmer just as quickly jumped off the tractor to remonstrate with Collins, who by this time had made a hasty retreat from the hayfield into his van heading for Mauchline.

On his return to Mauchline he was met by an irate John Pollock who told him in no uncertain terms his mistreatment of customers would not be tolerated. The upshot of this incident led to John Pollock and Jim Marr arriving at Kilmarnock and repairing the baler themselves.

Throughout 1973 and 1974, I was very happy being the first point of contact for many farmer customers who came into the store for spares/repairs and enquiries for new machines. Such enquires were passed to J. McCulloch, Ian Bryan or John Pollock.

During this era, John Pollock also developed a metal detector - the Agritec. The purpose of the detector was to alert the operator when metal was present within the Swath. Around 20-30 of these units were sold. Interest was shown within the agricultural field, however it later transpired that New Holland had already been working on an integrated system and production was halted.

More good news was to follow on a personal level in 1975 with the birth of our only daughter, Alison, who arrived into the world on 11 February, weighing a healthy 6lb 10 oz. Who would have thought some 27 years later she was to become part of the fabric of Pollock Farm Equipment Ltd?

Into 1975, we were still working on 1974 orders when a further fifty units were ordered, namely, numbers 1401-1450. This would be the last Japanese order for byre cleaners. John Pollock, and his wife Margaret, visited Japan in 1972, primarily to see if there were more opportunities for Pollock

Machines in Japan and to see some of the more interesting installations.

Mr Hayashi took them to Otaru, where they saw a dairy farm with eighteen units installed with all the muck being cross-conveyed to a separator/drier and re-cycled and sold to Otaru. I was more impressed with the calculator they brought back. Costing over £60 or three weeks' wages for tradesmen, this was used in the drawing office.

4.17 Gearing in packing case, ready for export.

In the background, in 1975, John Pollock was in talks with the Japanese who by this time were preparing to build their own byre-cleaners. However, they had done such a good marketing job, it was thought to be foolish to sell anything other than Pollock machines. A deal was struck and the Pollock name could be used for marketing purposes and a payment would be made for each unit sold. In the early days of this agreement John commented that it was much easier than the hassle of exporting a product which required long lead times and was labour intensive. By the end of 1976, we had completed all the orders on hand and it would be a long time before any other export opportunities came along.

The table below shows the shipping dates, number of units, and serial numbers of our Japanese business.

| Destination | Machine Number | Shipping Date |
|---|---|---|
| Tokyo | 208-217 | 29 May 1967 |
| Tokyo | 301-314 | 21 March 1968 |
| Yokohama/Otaru | 400-409 | 14 May 1968 |
| Yokohama/Otaru | 430-439 | 26 June 1968 |
| Yokohama/Otaru | 461-470 | 18 December 1969 |
| Tokyo | 510-524 | 15 February 1970 |
| Yokohama | 531-540 | 15 June 1970 |
| Otaru | 560-591 | 16 July 1970 |
| Yokohama | 681-690 | 8 April 1971 |
| Otaru | 701-725 | 13 May 1971 |
| Otaru | 731-762 | 14 June 1971 |
| Otaru | 821-830 | 29 October 1971 |
| Otaru | 871-884 | 24 March 1972 |
| Otaru | 901-910 | 20 September 1972 |
| Kobe | 941-942 | 18 July 1972 (Special) |
| Otaru/Tokyo | 951-970 | 15 October 1972 |
| Kobe | 1001-1012 | 26 March 1973 |
| Otaru | 1031-1040 | 14 May 1973 |
| Yokohama/Otaru | 1051-1096 | 11 July 1973 |
| Yokohama | 1101-1104 | 29 September 1973 |
| Otaru | 1111-1130 | 23 October 1973 |
| Yokohama/Kobe/Otaru | 1141-1180 | 12 October 1973 |
| Otaru | 1191/1199 | 28 September 1973 |
| Otaru/Kobe/Tokyo | 1200-1240 | 21 March 1974 |
| Otaru/Kobe | 1262-1269 | 14 June 1974 |
| Otaru/Kobe | 1270-1281 | 15 August 1974 |
| Otaru/Kobe | 1283-1300 | 15 August 1974 |
| Yokohama/Otaru/Kobe | 1401-1450 | February 1975 |

4.18 John Pollock in Japan with a Pollock's byre cleaner, c. 1970

With the end of the Japanese orders, we were still selling byre cleaners all over Great Britain, especially in large pig units which were springing up all around the country. By the end of the 1970s, we were selling less and less byre cleaners and in 1984, we reached Machine No. 1980, for the North of Scotland College of Agriculture in an Embryo Transplant Unit. Machine No. 1973 was installed in Yorkshire TV'S 'Emmerdale Farm' where I met all the actors, including those who played Seth, Joe Sugden, Annie Sugden and Amos. This machine appeared in the opening credits for a considerable time. The customer was Arthur Peel of Lindley farm (Near Otley).

My hard work and loyalty had not gone unnoticed and towards the end of 1975, John Pollock suggested that instead of coming into the office every time a customer enquired about a machine, he would give me a confidential list of the nett buying price of everything in stock and the price expected and it would be left up to me to agree a price which suited

111

4.19 John Pollock, taken in 1973

both the customer and the company. This was a task I relished and set me on a career I had only dreamed of. Around the same time, John asked me to go out and price a new machine along with a trade in value of the existing machine. After much debate with the farmer, the order was secured and his old machine traded in and on to the next sale.

December of that year saw John purchasing a new car and from 5 January 1976, I had to go out on the road as a Retail Salesman. Incidentally, the car was a Vauxhall Chevette hatchback which cost £1,551. I was assigned East and North Ayrshire and John McCulloch covered South Ayrshire. Sales

4.20 Lorry with Japanese exports, 1967.

of balers, foragers and so on were buoyant. Throughout this period the retail workshop was busy as ever, but storm clouds were gathering over the manufacturing business.

The Pollocks had always gone to Smithfield Show from 1903 through to 1939 as exhibitors, and thereafter as visitors, to do business with their many trade contacts. In December 1976, along with Jim Marr, Ian Bryan and myself, we headed for Central Station, Glasgow, where we boarded the Caledonian Sleeper to London. We went straight to Earls Court to meet with John and Margaret Pollock, who had gone to London a few days before. At the show, it was an amazing affair with all manner of exhibits, with most of the up to date tractors and implements on show.

The show had left us on a high, and having purchased a new suit for the show, we were invited to meet the Pollocks at the Kensington Close for dinner. If truth be told, we had consumed copious amounts of alcohol during the day which had left us feeling rather merry. On to Kensington Close Hotel where I met Mrs Pollock, whose first words to me were, 'Lovely suit, James, pity about your zip.' I was mortified and apologised profusely. That night was to remain ever embedded as after a lovely meal, we took a taxi back to the hotel. Ian Bryan stumbled going into the taxi and had to be assisted by Mrs Pollock's boot, which did the job, and we took the short journey back to our hotel.

This experience was to prove to be an invaluable one as shortly after I faced the wrath of John Pollock who informed me it was unacceptable and unprofessional to drink at any show where business was being conducted. This is a life lesson I have carried through the years and now, almost fifty years later, I stand by his policy.

John Pollock had for some time noticed the decline of the dairy byres in favour of loose housing systems where the cows were free to roam the cowshed and have defined feeding passages with separate sleeping areas. Alfa-Laval had patented a scraper for this type of shed in the 1960s and one or two of their systems were sold and installed by Pollocks. This prompted John to look seriously at manufacturing a system based on the byre cleaners of 1962.

4.21 Old office before 1970 upstairs addition.

4.22 Mounted Disc Harrow, 1950.

In 1977, A. & W. Pollock Ltd started the development of a passage scraper system utilising as much of the technology used in the byre cleaner. Various types of drive systems were tried out including a reciprocating drive with limit switches fore and aft travel. This was later abandoned in favour of an open drive unit with gears and shafts like the one which had been so successful on the byre cleaner. It was decided that we could modify the chain to run on the surface by welding blocks on the drop forged links and use the same riveting process as used on the byre cleaner for test purposes.

Before deciding to commission a new forged link for scrapers, it was agreed to weld blocks to the existing ones to make a chain link of the correct specification, the corner idlers could be modified for scrapers simply utilising the same castings as before. All scraper systems have four corners, a drive unit, lengths of chain and two scraper blades, and of course the brains of the system, the control panel. John, whose electrical knowledge was second to none, designed the control panel and by now we were ready to build a test rig. This was done in the factory, however, with the electrical regulation becoming stricter, this job was farmed out to Aird Walker & Ralston (Kilmarnock).

After some early setbacks in 1978, we now had a working full-sized passage scraper system and now the quest was on to find a suitable customer requiring a scraper system to test the suitability of such a machine.

In early 1979, I was tasked with finding a customer requiring a scraper system which by this time was up and running, but to keep it very quiet in case of problems. An advert was placed in a well-known farming newspaper, being specifically vague about what was proposed, and within a day of the advert being placed, we had a very local customer querying what was on offer. I immediately suggested that I visit the farm and discuss our proposals. This was accepted and we had a site for our first passage scraper system.

Things were not going well in the retail or manufacturing sectors. The year 1978 was poor for byre cleaner sales and, although we had a new scraper system, we could not sustain the workforce at present levels. This meant the dreaded redundancies for the first time were on the horizon.

It transpired that my younger brother Gerry, who by that time was time-served, Willie Baird, Willie Ferguson, who was in the stores, and Beth Foster from the office, all had to be

4.23 Trailer Disc Harrow, 1950.

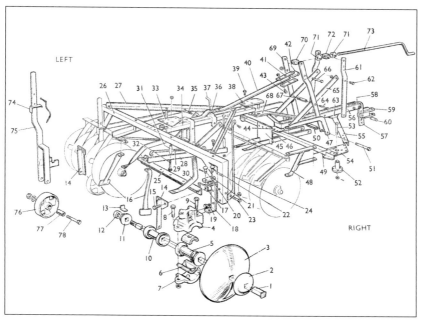

4.24 Trailer Disc Harrow – exploded view from parts list, 1950.

made redundant.  By the time 1980 came around, John was totally disillusioned with the retail division, with New Holland whom we had represented since the demise of A. Jack & Co (Maybole) dictating stock, stock order and new machine targets. Enough was enough.

Jim Marr had a distinguished career with the company from 1955, working through the ranks.  His position was changed and he was now required to go out on the road as a salesman/engineer, covering the position previously held by John McCulloch.  He returned to his former job as foreman in 1979.

Mr Watson of Barboigh farm, Mauchline, agreed to be the site for our first scraper installation.  This system was completed and installed in September of 1979.  The long process of research and development was now over, but the system had now to prove itself suitable for the job in hand.

Our next plan in action was to inform the Department of Agriculture and Fisheries for Scotland that we had a full size working installation of an Automatic Scraper system in operation. Within a fortnight, we had a deputation of Agricultural Advisers and Planners, as well as Mr Reid, the Head of the DAFS, to see the system in action and to prove it suitable. Approval of this system for grant aid allowed farmers to include Scraper Systems in their six-year plans under the new Farm and Horticultural Development Scheme (FHDS) supported by the European Union. This system worked very well and we were receiving enquiries for scrapers on a weekly basis.

Life must go on, and throughout 1979 and 1980, I was occupying my time between retail sales and manufacturing, with John covering the north of the country and me increasing in the south, both selling direct where we had no agent or through a dealership. As our product was receiving good reviews up and down the country, my time was taken up mainly by dealers who were receiving enquiries on a weekly basis. One of the first dealers were Rickerby Ltd, operating from their installations apartment at Currock Road (Carlisle). However, with depots at Dumfries, Annan, Carlisle, Penrith and Cockermouth, each with their own local representative pulling in enquiries, I was kept very busy.

Rickerby Ltd had been agents for Andrew Pollock for many products and had sold his equipment for over one hundred years with great success. Joseph Hillary, another old established company, had sold many byre cleaners and who had been receiving a few enquiries were also appointed as agents, but many of the companies which previously sold our machines were now agents of competitor's machines.

At the 1980 Highland Show, we were exhibiting both the byre cleaner and Pollock passage scraper, the latter received some ninety-six enquires for systems in cow, pig and poultry units. We exhibited at the Royal Highland Show, the

118

Yorkshire Show at Harrogate, the Royal Show at Stoneleigh, and the Dairy Event, as well as many more regional and county shows. The All-Ireland Ploughing Match was a new outlet for us, exhibiting at various agents' stands over the next few years.

4.25 A Pollock's scraper installed at Strathearn Pig Producers, near Crieff, c. 1970,

With business steady, but still requiring growth, our next problem was to decide on the production targets for 1980-81. We concluded that we should build five units on a pre-production run and for 1981-2, build twenty-five units. Ian Alexander of Cluny Crichton farm (Banchory), our local vet, David Alexander's brother, had built a new Cubicle Unit in 1978. David of course told Ian about the new developments he had seen at Pollocks. Soon an appointment was made for John Pollock to go to Banchory to discuss the requirements. Subsequently, units numbered 2, 3 & 4 were ordered. This was a conventional four-passage system with two cubicle passages to the extremities of the shed and two passages either side of the central tractor passage. This was a traditional layout, normally scraping into a slatted tank. However, with rock present within one foot of the surface, a gravity flow channel was not an option. Therefore, we built a byre cleaner to work in a shallow channel to act as a gutter cleaner, thus giving a new lease of life to a machine built in 1962.

Although byre cleaner sales were now a thing of the past, with the introduction of our passage scraper system, we sold a fair number of cross-conveyors. In all around one hundred to work in conjunction with passage scrapers. We also tackled some industrial jobs, most notably some cross conveyors for the St Regis Paper Co. in Taplow, Essex. One of the managers from this company rented a farm cottage at Drumrennan for his summer break. This farm had a byre cleaner installed in the dairy byre and the manager was amazed at how efficiently the machine operated. He took the telephone number off the transmission cover and contacted us on his return to work. John Pollock travelled down, saw what was required, was sure our equipment was satisfactory and the order was secured.

Our main competitor in the early days of passage scrapers was Alfa-Laval and we were flattered to receive quite a few orders for cross conveyors from the company that we considered to be our main competitors. Quality Equipment of Bury St Edmunds were also another company which sold cross conveyors, mainly in poultry units along with Wadland Bros. who built many pig units in England.

Cross conveyors were not entirely unknown. In the modern poultry units these were installed at the end of the run of cages which housed the hens. The muck from the cages was deposited into a narrow gutter on the outside of the shed, fed into an elevator and discharged into a muck spreader.

The next unit sold was a three-passage system for W. R. Campbell, Low Holehouse farm (Mauchline). Hard on the heels of this came our first attempt at a low level slatted unit for R. L. Montgomerie. J. Harvie, Whitehill (Drongan), provided the first set up to test three-phase power.

Machine numbers 101-105 were our largest project to date. It comprised of eight runs of slats 150 feet long, scraping the muck from an eighteen inch deep cellar directly into a cross conveyor, from there on to a reception tank where the cow muck was electrically pumped to an above ground slurry store. We were scraping muck from 800 head of young stock into a cross-conveyor and pumped it to a store without ever being manually handled. This installation was the first for Mr Campbell Graham, Aucheneck Estates, Croftamie. It proved so successful that in subsequent years we have sold the same customer a further fifteen scraping systems. Now, almost 37 years later, this system is still used daily, and in that time only the chain, scraper blades and corner pulleys have been replaced. The original drive units and control panels are still working away satisfactorily.

System number 106 was sold to J. Templeton, Barglachan farm, (Auchinleck). This unit was curious as much as instead of fitting superior chain all round, we installed half superior chain and half economy chain. Until this point, all machines were supplied with either full superior or else full economy chain. This option was becoming the norm, and all machines sold today are half superior and half economy

Machine No. 123 went to the Rowett Research Institute (Bucksburn), who previously used byre cleaners in their metabolic research units.

Throughout the 1980s we exhibited regularly at the Dairy Event at Stoneleigh, also the Royal Show, the Royal Lancashire Show, the Cheshire Ploughing Match, the Great Yorkshire Show and the Royal Cornwall Show, either with our own stand or as part of an agent's stand.

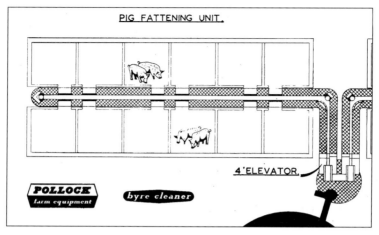

4.26 Sketch of Pig Fattening Unit.

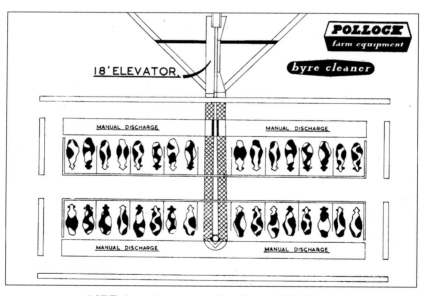

4.27 Dairy set up, as used on Emmerdale Farm.

The mid- to late-seventies had seen unprecedented improvements in agriculture and probably the most significant was the introduction of self-propelled forage harvesters and John Pollock had been instrumental in introducing such machines to Ayrshire. He sold the first machine, a New Holland self-propelled Forest Harvester, to T. & J. Neil, Contractors, of Shawwood (Catrine), and many more were to follow with Archie Wilson of Millmannoch and D. & R. McInnes from Grassyards (Kilmarnock) and Jim Mair, Agricultural Contractor (Drongan), all purchasing machines.

Self-propelled forage harvester machines were capable of more than sixty acres per day, the average farmer on a big day would probably do six or seven acres and require a one hundred horsepower tractor as well. This more than anything caused the demise of the retail business. However, it was not the last we would hear of Jim Marr. With hindsight, it is easy to work out why these decisions had to be made.

In 1981, the decision was made to close the retail department and make the retail staff redundant.

As everyone was going about their business, unbeknown to me, in the background, Jim Marr was already planning his next move. He approached John Pollock with the proposal that he could rent the retail stores, showroom and workshop and continue much as before. John agreed to this proposal and J. & P. Marr Ltd was born. Jim Marr set off with himself, Robert Smith in the stores and son Alan Marr in the workshop. He retained the Lister agency, the Fiat Tractor franchise, which Pollock had held for a few years, along with the Kew power washers and Gray's of Fetterangus for buckrakes, land rollers and push-off buckrakes.

# CHAPTER FIVE

# 1981-1998 John Pollock (Mauchline) Ltd

In 1981 A. & W. Pollock became John Pollock (Mauchline) Ltd, to reflect the changes which had been made, and of course the ownership of the company. Andrew Pollock, who started business in 1867 and continued until his death in 1904. His widow, Martha Pollock, supervised until 1914, when Andrew and William Pollock were old and experienced enough to take over the reins from the management who had ran the business since Andrew's demise. Thereafter the two sons ran the business until 1981.

The early eighties were good business-wise. With no retail department, our concentration was focused on producing automatic scrapers. Ian Bryan retired on 2 May 1981. He had joined A. & W. Pollock in the early 1930s as a clerical assistant and ended up as a director of A. & W. Pollock. The following Monday he was back at work as normal and told John Pollock he wasn't ready to retire and perhaps he could find something for him to do. John duly obliged and set Ian up in the former sales office, building control panels for scraper systems, where he remained for the next few years. Ian Bryan could not take things easier from his official retiral, nor take an occasional day off, and he died suddenly in the Cowgate in Mauchline, on the way from work, aged 75.

In November 1983 we were looking for a panel builder/electrical engineer and The Training Centre in Irvine had a likely candidate, a young man from Auchinleck, Reid Armour. After doing some background checks with Auchinleck Academy, Reid was offered the job and now, some 34 years later, he still occupies the same position.

With Davy Goudie overseeing the manufacturing, David Russell was promoted from the workshop floor to foreman, having responsibility for all installations and service work, as well as keeping a record of the machines installed. After the success of the cow brushes, he developed a rotary cow brush powered by a motor of one half horse power. This brush worked very well and we sold a few however, with driving through a gearbox meant costs were too high and within a few years, most of the cow shed equipment suppliers were offering similar brushes at much lower prices.

The EEC had announced dairy milk quotas would be introduced in early 1984. This proclamation had dairy farmers in a quandary, either take the golden handshake and switch to beef production or continue in dairying and produce 10% less milk than the year before. Our records showed that following this declaration, our fledging scraper business was slashed by 50% and 1985 proved to be just as tough as the 1970s had been for us. The result of this was to see few opportunities and markets for our products.

---

*John and Margaret Pollock*
*request the pleasure of the company of*

.......................................................................

*at a PARTY and PRESENTATION*
*at Haplan*
*on Saturday, 2nd May, 1981*
*to mark the Retiral of Ian Bryan from*
**A. & W. POLLOCK LTD.**

*R.S.V.P.*
*Haplan*
*Mauchline*                                              *8.00 p.m.*

---

3.09 Ideal Potato Digger, c. 1928.

126

Around this time, we appointed a new agency in Northern Ireland - Inter Link Systems - who were main agents for the Hunday Feed Systems. Visiting dairy farms daily, this certainly suited our business model and being a young and ambitious company was a bonus. Byre cleaners had sold in Northern Ireland but not in any great numbers as this had been due to political unrest.

Not long after Wilbur McConkie of Churchtown had ordered a system (Number 322) from Interlink, we received an enquiry from County Cork. Taggarts (Ireland) Ltd, who imported the very successful Enkamat Cow Cubicle Mattress System, were interested in selling our scrapers in the Republic of Ireland. I was dispatched to County Cork to meet William Walsh (Taggerts). His knowledge of the area and its dairy farmers was second to none as he had previously been sales manager with Lucy & O'Connell, the main Alfa-Laval dealers for the Cork area.

It must be noted that at the time, dairying in Ireland was going through a transition, with many new diary units being built and the average production was well behind the UK at around 950 gallons per cow. This was to alter dramatically in the next few years. Our Northern Ireland agent was selling an increasing number of systems and a fellow Northern Ireland manufacturer was heavily involved in new Turnkey projects in Saudi Arabia.

Normally for these units, everything from buildings to cubicles, dairy parlours, wash down systems, scrapers and all other ancillary equipment were sourced in Northern Ireland and shipped to Saudi Arabia.

Pollock scrapers were chosen for this project and sent to Northern Ireland for containerising and delivery straight to the farm. To the Riyadh area of Saudi Arabia, this order for three systems was despatched, and further orders were secured and in total fifteen units were sent to Saudi Arabia.

Not to be outdone by their Northern Irish counterparts, Taggart IRL had been working on a large Canadian Government contract for the supply of Enkamat, scrapers, cubicles etc. With the order secured, we were trying to plan for the control panels, times and motor. However, we found that the Canadian power supply was not standardised throughout Canada as in the UK. In the UK, we have 220 volts or 415 volts – 3 phase, unlike Canada who used 120/208 volts or 240/480 volts or 347/600 volts at 60 Hz. This was a nightmare, so we built the controllers to the UK specifications and sourced a transformer to convert the local Canadian supply to the UK standard. This, in fact, meant that the Canadian machines would now run on standard controllers and motors. This huge project was completed on time and shipped out to Vancouver Island.

On one hand, a manufacturing business making a reasonable profit and on the other hand, we had a loss-making retail business. In the same year, I transferred from retail sales to manufacturing sales. To say I was disappointed would be an understatement as I had worked hard and had a good relationship with many of my customers.

Throughout the 1980s, we had a fairly stable workforce with Wullie Holland, Jimmy Sloan, George Findlay and Billy Walker, being joined by new boys, Martin Waddell, Arthur Cummings, Norman Anderson and Reid Armour. Martin Waddell started in November 1981, firstly as a 'Yopper', on the Government's Youth Opportunities Programme, and by June 1982, started a four-year apprenticeship. John started a lot of boys on the YOP scheme and to his credit, not one finished after their six months' stint – all were retained and given apprenticeships. Norrie, a native of Turriff, joined in April 1982, and Reid came from the Ayrshire Group Training Services starting on 9 January 1984. Norman was plunged in at the deep end and was soon all over the country installing and commissioning scraper systems along with Wullie Holland.

At the Royal Highland Show, 1984, we exhibited passage scrapers, byre cleaners, cow brushes, slurry grids and, on occasions, a slurry separator. In the late 1950s, we were known for implements, carts, trailers, potato diggers and harrows but through the influence of John Pollock and since 1958, the company had reinvented itself as a major player in the fixed equipment for animal sheds of all descriptions.

In the autumn of 1984, our workforce has been trimmed again, sales of scrapers had been buoyant during 1983 and were approximately 140 systems. 1984 saw a decrease of over 50% with only around sixty-five systems sold. With a total workforce of around twenty, the writing was surely on the wall and a decision was made to cut four jobs. Two of these positions were former apprentices, who by now were time served, namely Ronnie Pettigrew from Mauchline, and Robert Britten who travelled from Kirkconnel. The other two were Danny O'Donnell, and Auchinleck man Bobby Wallace, who were labourer/machine operators.

Jean Watson had been in the office since the early 70s. She was getting married to John Mair, Tabbochburn, Mauchline, so there was shortly to be a vacancy. My sister Anne, who had been a clerical assistant at Currie's of Auchinleck before moving to London, decided to come home and applied for a job along with Gerry and me. She started in November 1977 and left to get married in 1985 to be replaced by Lorna Rae of Catrine.

By now most of the institutes in the country were involved in various projects and seeking some advice, especially at the North of Scotland College of Agriculture and the Rowett Research Institute. John Pollock went to both these units, one a low level slatted unit, by which time we had gained some expertise, and the other was a study of rabbits, their habits and the suitability of a commercial rabbit breeding unit. John was successful on both accounts and we installed both units a short time later. Our first commercial rabbit unit was installed in Cheshire some months later for Hy-line Rabbits.

I had always imagined that the rabbits would be produced for the dog and cat food industry, however, I learned, this was not the case. All of the rabbits produced by this unit were exported to France for human consumption and only the hearts, kidneys and liver were sold on to the processors of dog and cat food.

Machine number 170 was basically a conventional scraper system, installed in a low level slatted unit, driven from above the slats down onto a cornea sprocket, with the sprocket and corner idlers submerged below three feet of slurry. This system was supposed to work with gravity but in practice all the urine ran off and the solids were left behind and the customer was unable to draw off the solids with conventional machines. We set about designing a set of agitators to go up and down through the slurry, not allowing it to separate, keeping it liquid. The theory behind this installation was that when heavy frost occurred, this machine could be switched to automatic and left overnight to prepare the slurry for spreading. It is significant to note that this unit had another three same systems of the same installed. The operators of this unit were the well-known sheep exporters G. & D. Vivers of Dornockstown, Annan.

Back to business and by 10 October 1983 we reached 250 units sold with that unit being installed in a beef unit for Russel and Isobel McNab of Garlaff farm, Cumnock.

My change in job description had its perks and I could travel a lot more. John and I went to Denmark to gauge the type of machines that they were making and what was selling in that country. We visited two manufacturers in Denmark and various research establishments. Always looking for inspiration, we saw many types of scrapers, rope, hydraulic and chain, with a variety of slurry handling systems. The hydraulic system impressed us, in operation stroking at almost one metre with very heavy blades and a track fabricated from two 'C' sections welded together with holes approximately one metre apart and powered by a three-horse power motor attached to a hydraulic pump.

5.02 Prototype of Slurry Loader, operated by three horsepower motor, c. 1982.

On our return from Denmark, we started to look seriously at the rod scraper system, using a gearbox to drive the track rather than hydraulic. Quite a few of these systems were sold and for a single passage were ideal. The more passages installed required a drive unit, motor and controller making us very uncompetitive.

At the Royal Show in 1985, I counted fourteen different Hydraulic Scraper Systems on show, of these only around four or five manufacturers compete in the scraper business. Today, most of these systems are of Irish extraction.

The Paris show was always a favourite of John Pollock and his wife Margaret and he went over to see what was happening in Europe.

John was a regular visitor to the Sima exhibition in the Paris Exhibition Centre at the Porte De Versailles and in 1985 he saw a cow grooming brush on a stand and thought it may well be the sort of item which would capture the imagination of our many dairy farmers. A deal was struck and the cow brush was duly dispatched to the implement works for us to do some tests with it. Robert Sloan of Darnlaw farm (Auchinleck) was chosen as the test bed for this project.

The cows were soon using the brush daily and certainly looked much better with the brush cleaning dust and dirt from their coats. We imported a pallet load of brushes but the frames were flimsily built and breakages were happening regularly. The decision was made to fabricate our own frame and continue to buy the brushes from France. This worked well for a time but soon the British brush manufacturers were offering us a suitable product at a good price. This allowed us to proudly boast a British product. The first hundred sets of cow brushes we sold took about a year to sell but after that, following a very successful campaign in the dairy farm magazine, we literally sold thousands of brushes. Even today, over thirty-five years later, we still sell between fifty to one hundred sets of cow brushes. We also managed to sell one hundred sets of cow brushes to Cornes and Co of Japan.

Having picked up the cow brush in 1985, John was always on the lookout for the next big thing in cow shed development - but so were hundreds of other manufacturers.

At the 1985 Winter Fair in Ingliston, we sold forty-three cow brushes from the stand. We were also at the Royal Highland, Great Yorkshire and Ayr shows. Each show yielded good sales and follow-up orders, a great benefit to the company.

From December 1985, through to August 1986, we supplied no fewer than 750 passage scraper machines, many of them to existing customers returning for a second or third time. We supplied the new pig unit at Tillycorthie with four systems, and the Scottish Agricultural College at Dumfries with a total of eight machines.

However, our biggest break came with an enquiry for a new farm being built at Roden Estate, near Telford in Shropshire. I met with the South West Dairy Manager, and discussed our proposals, measured up and produced a quotation for suitable equipment. We heard nothing for around two weeks, then I received a phone call. The South West Dairy Manger, Roger Smith, requested a meeting at Roden Estate and a deal was concluded on my second visit. Never one to miss an opportunity, and always able to hold a good conversation, whilst there, Roger Smith told me that Co-operative Wholesale Society were constantly improving their dairy units at their Down Ampney Estate (Cirencester) and Frisby Lodge (Leicester), and if our units were successful at Roden, there was potential for a few more units.

Within a few months, I was back to Cirencester discussing layouts for Church Farm (Latton) next door to CWS Creamery at Down Ampney. Again, our quotation was accepted and another job secured. In all we supplied forty-nine scraper systems to Co-operative Wholesale Society farms.

We reached a landmark in January 1986, passing the 500 mark for these scraper systems, with an export order for Masstock, Saudi Arabia, and three years later the markets were surely improving and we had sold our 750th unit, this time to the Kingdom of Fife, an area not noted for dairy farms. However, the few units in Fife were all large producers of milk, such as the Lyle family who had moved from Cambuslang to Leven some years earlier.

Around September 1986, we had an enquiry for a scraper system from Craggs of Conder Green – a small but very active dealer in Lancashire. With scrapers now being sold in most dairying areas, we appointed Craggs as agents. They still operate in Lancashire and still sell our scraper systems today.

Craggs of Conder Green consisted of Dave Hogarth, a young and ambitious salesman/engineer; twins, Ian and Barry Cragg; David Cragg; and cousin Andrew on fabrication work and Maurice Cragg, the company's founder at the helm. Craggs had come through the boom years of the seventies but, due to milk quotas, their business had suffered, but by late 1986 was slowly but surely recovering. However, winters were proving to be really tough.

This appointment proved crucial for both our successes with Craggs going on to be our top dealer. We now were working mainly on the west of the country where most of the dairy cows were concentrated with good representation in Cumberland, Westmoreland, Northumberland, Lancashire, Yorkshire, Cheshire and Shropshire. But we were not finished yet – we extended even further by appointing agents in Kent, Dorset, Hampshire and Devon.

By 1987, John and myself visited Cheshire to investigate the possibility of appointing a new agent as we felt we were not getting our fair share of the market due to increasing competition. No sooner had we returned to Mauchline when we received a phone call from Alistair King of R. T. C. Agricultural with an enquiry for a scraper system. An appointment was made and I went down to Frodsham, where R. T. C. were based, and met with Alistair King, who by this time had three jobs for me to see. Alistair King was the Sales Manager for a father and son business, namely Jack and Adrian Oldfield of the Runcorn Trading Company (R. T. C.).

On returning to the office, I produced drawings of the various layouts I had seen, priced up each job and waited.

Within three days, Alastair King phoned me with news that he sold two of the three units priced.

Making that sale and building the relationship took time. Machines such as byre cleaners, automatic scrapers and fixed equipment were great money earners, but the negotiations had to be dealt with respectfully and professionally. This, I have learned over the years, is how you build a strong foundation and a lasting relationship with your clients. In the early days, a sketch plan accompanied each quote and showed the location of the implements. There were onsite visits, telephone calls and much negotiation before the business transaction was concluded. An enjoyable experience, but one which involved a great deal of hard work.

By the Royal Highland Show of 1986, we had now been exhibiting our passage scraper system for five years and, apart from the hiccup in 1984 due to quotas, the business was back on track with sales growing a pace.

Reid Armour and Norman Anderson had been to Robert Kerr in Auchengree to fetch a batch of casting which were being keywayed by Kerr's. They were then diverted to Allan Cuthbertson of Stoneside farm (Busby) to repair a scraper system which had broken down. Never to be beaten and, knowing time was of the essence, Norrie decided that he would take a short cut to Stoneside farm via the back road which happened to have a ford. Little did he know that a fork in the road had led to such poor visibility that our truck missed the plinth and tipped over, landing right in the ford. Submerged in water, Norrie and Reid realised that they had to get out.

Norrie, rather vocal by this time, was beginning to unravel but quick acting Reid decided to stand on Norrie's shoulders and prised the door open making a safe exit for both men, albeit rather wet. The truck was not so lucky and was a write off. The story does not end there, as we had to hire a frogman to go into the ford and retrieved the castings, but Reid's prized possession, a wooden cabinet full of electrical tools and spares was last seen heading for Glasgow bobbing up and down in the river.

Business was good and by January 1989 we had reached machines numbered 1000-1003 with a large dairy unit at Dolphenby farm, Penrith sold by Rickerby's (Penrith branch). We had reached a marvellous milestone with this order but surely, we could not beat the total for byre cleaners of 2000.

Opportunities came out now and then, and to be able to welcome such breaks and reminisce all at the same time, was not something we could often do.

One such opportunity came our way in 1989. We heard a local famer had built and tested out a slurry agitator in his lagoon with remarkable results. John Caldwell of Ladyyard farm (Mauchline) had told me about this machine being built by Jimmy Smillie of West Doura - the very same farm James Carnduff had taken over the tenancy of in 1873. To be able to visit this farm was a privilege for the business.

The machine itself consisted of four flotation barrels mounted in a cross frame, with a drive shaft driven from above with three half barrels all angled to catch as much wind as possible through the drive shaft down to the impeller. This arrangement agitated the slurry sufficiently to keep it liquid and dispel the odour attached to slurry spreading.

John Pollock was a very shrewd and honest business man and immediately advised Jimmy Smillie to seek the advice of a patent agent. An appointment was made with the agent we used in Glasgow and both John and Jimmy went to the city with preliminary drawings and specifications for this machine.

In August 1989, we spoke to the local council to ask if we could possibly use the facilities at Cumnock swimming pool to do some further tests at the end of the swimming season and this was granted. We built a unit for test purposes using a passage scraper drive unit instead of the windmill in Jimmy Smillie's version and fitted a half-horsepower motor and taper lock pulleys to enable us to change both the input speed and output speed. We also made two large impellors that we could adjust the angles of to agitate the slurry.

The test at Cumnock proved very successful until we were interrupted by three old gentlemen on their daily stroll, one of whom commented, 'Never in all his life had he seen sic a Heath Robinson machine in the swimming pool.' Reid Armour and Robert Brown, both suited and booted for the water, were told by a bemused John Pollock, to pack up all their gear and we would see them back at Mauchline.

Back at Mauchline, we arranged to install the agitator in a working situation at Taylor's of Hill farm (Crossroads, near Mauchline), where the slurry in the tower was growing a fair crop of grass. We hired a crane to install the agitator in the slurry tower. Within a few minutes, the crust on the slurry started to break up and become mostly liquid. Within half an hour, the complete crust was gone. However, what happened next took us completely by surprise. With the slurry now liquid, the flotation barrels started to rotate anti-clockwise with the impellor going clockwise and shortly after this our patent agent reported back that a patent for a similar drive system had been applied for in America. The project was abandoned soon afterwards.

In 1988 a lull in business led to Jimmy Sloan and George Findlay leaving the company with a voluntary redundancy package, with Davie Russell also departing at this time.

It wasn't all work and no play in the late eighties and into the nineties. We had a very successful football team playing the agricultural league in the Super Shoot complex in Ayr. One incident amongst the many happened on 16 November

1993. Billy (Hooter) Houston came out of the goal mouth to block a ball, went head over heels and landed awkwardly. I was immediately summoned on to the field where Billy said he was hurt. I replied, 'Jist get up and stamp yer feet a couple of times ya big wooss'. However, on closer examination, I noticed that his ankle was at ninety degrees to his leg. We removed him from the field and finished the game. Billy was taken to hospital where he was detained for an operation the next morning to repair a broken leg and displaced ankle. It was then off to Auchinleck to inform Billy's mother why her son would not be home any time soon. Back to the factory on Tuesday morning and I had to inform John Pollock why we were a welder fabricator short for the foreseeable future. It was not all bad news as the season before we had won the Christmas Challenge Cup against the Hamilton Brothers Team. Local companies who competed were:

Andrew Alston & Son (Cumnock)
Hamilton Bros (Tarbolton)
Soil Fertility Dunns (Ayr)
And two or three Young Farmers' teams.

Never to be down hearted, the 1990s heralded new optimism for dairy farmers and many were planning new dairy units. By now some of the larger companies were offering scarifiers along with their slurry stores, slurry tankers, milking parlours such as Malgar, Boythorpe, Howard Harvestore, Alfa-Laval and Dairy Master. Even although our scrapers were consistently more expensive than others in the market, we sold our systems as built to a quality - never down to a price.

As the 1990s went on, we reached the fifteen hundreds with chain scrapers and by November 1994, with a local unit Number 1500 to J. Hunter & Co, Gargowan farm (Ochiltree) being sold.

The Royal Highland Show in 1992 gave us the opportunity to exhibit a slurry separator manufactured by Farmers Build. This was a running exhibit showing how the separator actually worked, but the smell of the slurry only added to the ambiance of the exhibition. We also displayed this separator on a few occasions after 1992.

We were quite successful in selling slurry separators, and in fact we sold one on the Isle of Mull, where the dairy farmer was marketing his milk and cheese.

Around 1993, after a great deal of work at the Co-op, Martin Waddell, Billy Houston and Reid Armour left Mauchline, arriving at Bridgend Garage at Auchinleck to fill up with fuel. Martin inadvertently put petrol in the tank but noticing his mistake after about six or seven litres decided it would be fine to now fill the remainder with diesel.

The team began travelling down the M6 and then to the M5, heading towards Strensham Services. On reaching an incline towards Strensham, they were suddenly passed by a Reliant Robin on the motorway – this was to give them some indication that all was not well.

Andrew Pollock was dispatched with a replacement truck, travelling overnight, arriving in Cirencester at 5 o'clock in the morning. Martin and Billy Houston travelled in the back of the truck rather than face Andrew. Reid then drove all four to the C. W. S. down at Ampney, then on to Swindon Station for Andrew to take the long journey home by train.

Martin was half of one set of twins employed by the firm, Douglas Govan being another half of a second set. The longer that I live, the more I am convinced that in some instances, twins share a brain. Martin and Douglas brought a great amount to the firm including many funny stories that I can recount and share in this book.

In addition to the many funny stories we could share, we also had our fair share of sadness. Driving home from the Highland Show, John informed me that his wife was very ill and he would be spending more time at home until his wife got better and I would be required to take the helm for the foreseeable future. Mrs Pollock was seen by many doctors during this time but unfortunately the outlook was not good and sadly she passed away in September 1994. John took a very long time to recover from Margaret's death, if ever. Throughout the time, he was supported by his daughter Jane and son Andrew. Andrew, who had been working at the factory for some time, took over as secretary the day Mrs Pollock died. Computers being his chosen profession, he set about revolutionising our ageing computer systems to great effect.

In August 1995, the company purchased another vehicle, this time a Nissan Cabstar. Now the pride of our fleet, the Nissan was out on one of its very first jobs for the C. W. S. at Frisby Lodge. A team of three engineers, Norman Anderson, John Gibson Jnr and Martin Waddell, who was charged with handling this new piece of equipment, set out after the installation to their hotel in Market Harborough where they consumed a Chinese meal, washed down with a large amount of alcohol.

A ringing telephone woke me up at around 11.30pm with a call from a very sheepish Martin Waddell, claiming to have mislaid the truck. My first question was, 'Please tell me it is the old truck,' – Oh no! Not to do anything by half, Martin had only gone and lost the new truck, unmarked, unlettered and prior to this incident relatively unscathed. Following this mishap Martin on his visit to Market Harborough chained the truck to a bollard.

Realising that I was now charged with the task of relaying the news to John Pollock, I arrived at the offices rather pensively. As you can imagine, John did not take the news well.  Contacting the police at Market Harborough, he was assured that the police would do their best to locate the truck.

Some two days later, the grim news from Market Harborough reached Pollocks.  The news was not good.  Our truck had been found – minus engine, gearbox, seats, steering wheels and tyres, in a disused layby on the road south to Market Harborough.  It was agreed that picking up the shell of Martin's adventures served no purpose and the company were forced to write this off as a bad experience! Following this mishap, Martin, on his subsequent visits to Market Harborough, used a length of scraper chain securely fitted around a bollard and secured with a padlock to the axle of the truck to prevent the same happening again!

October 1995 saw another opportunity come our way as we received an enquiry from N. Griffin for four systems in a large cubicle unit for water buffalo.  The basis of his calculations was a good water buffalo in milk would produce approximately 2000 litres of milk per lactation against 7500 litres for a dairy cow, with a price of 85p per litre for buffalo milk and 25p per litre for cow's milk.

Great idea, some would say, and this seemed alright in practice but in the long term, could buffalo become more popular than cows?  This system was very well planned with no BSE among Buffalos, a ready supply of dairies wanting the milk for mozzarella production, with the milk being separated and dried, bagged up for gardeners and sold throughout the country as Buffalo Gold.  How could this fail?

Another very interesting project came along the following year – 1996. This involved us using a low level slatted scraper unit scraping the muck from a shed which had been adapted for rearing young ostriches.  The mature ostriches were kept in trios and grazed on the pasture with the only feed additive being type 1 granite rocks to aid their digestive systems.  The eggs were collected from the trios and taken to an incubator for hatching, with the young chicks being removed from the incubator and on to the purpose built shed for rearing.

Whilst on the farm, the farmer, Mr Walter Murray of Burnhouse (near Duns) showed us round the setup, letting us see his abattoir, and he told us that the average mature bird would yield approximately 250 kg of red meat. Another figure often misquoted is that a hen could lay between 80-100 eggs per season. While it is possible, in theory it is very much at the top end figure.

Before leaving Burnhouse, Walter Murray gave my wife some ostrich steak, burgers and sausages to try out – one of the few perks of the job. The end of 1997 saw us reach machine Number 1750. Although sales had now slowed dramatically, we were still pushing towards 2000 units sold, therefore beating the previous byre cleaner sales.

# CHAPTER SIX

# 1998-2017 Pollock Farm Equipment Ltd

In the summer of 1996, John Pollock asked both myself and Reid Armour to wait until after closing time. Neither of us had any inkling of what was about to be proposed. John explained that his son Andrew was not interested in making a career in agriculture and would much rather seek a career in computing, in which he had gained his degree whilst studying at the University of Glasgow.

John was very well liked and respected so we knew to call us into the office it had to be serious and serious he was. John stated that he was not prepared to 'die in harness' like his father had done some fifteen years earlier. He was keen to keep the business in safe hands and was offering us a life changing opportunity. After some discussion, John suggested we meet his accountant in Glasgow to discuss the complexity of transferring the business and continuing or restricting the business in our own right.

Next on the agenda was to meet with the company's bankers, the Royal Bank of Scotland in Cumnock. We duly arrived at the bank, who were sympathetic and listened to our proposals. We also each prepared a financial statement of our assets and liabilities, all to no avail, for we received a letter two days later from the bank telling us that this project was a nonstarter. So, it was back to the drawing board, with no Plan 'B', in our mind, we had to abandon our plans to take over the business.

Meanwhile, John Pollock actively started to look for a buyer who would buy the company, retain the work force and continue to trade as we had done for the last 130 years. I accompanied John on two occasions to visit agricultural

6.01 Jimmy McGhee

manufacturers, who might just solve the problem and either amalgamate the businesses or take us over. After some negotiations, both companies withdrew, so we were left back at square one.

For the next few months, we worked steadily, getting as many orders as possible and fulfilling these as quickly as possible. Knowing that John wished to retire in 1998, in October 1997, I met with another Pollock – George Pollock, who I had met at a pigeon show. George had recently retired from his position as manager of the Bank of Scotland in East Kilbride. He inquired after the business and I told him of the uncertainty of the company, certainly in the long term. He suggested that he could be of assistance, to give him a ring and we could meet up and discuss things further.

With a mixture of excitement and trepidation, I walked into the office on the Monday morning, and told John Pollock of my encounter with George Pollock. His response was that if we could work out a suitable strategy, he would certainly make things easy for us as his main concern was the continuing employment of the staff. I met with George Pollock and he requested sight of five years of business transactions, the financial statements and the current orders in hand. This was provided to him and George intimated that he needed one week to study these. Good as his word, George reported back to me within the week stating that it was not the best set of finances he had seen, but it was a long way off being the worst in his experience.

Things were moving fast and thankfully with the support of my wife Effie, I had the courage of my convictions to continue. Our next move was to appoint a chartered accountant, produce a proper business plan and of course seek loans, grants and funding wherever possible. George Pollock set up a meeting with East Ayrshire Council, the West of Scotland Loan Fund and the Bank of Scotland's small firms loan guarantee scheme, and at long last we appeared to be making progress. By mid-February, we had all the funding in place and John Pollock drew up a minute of agreement which my solicitor looked over. A few minor amendments were made to this document to suit both parties.

During negotiations, we took the time to identify all the plant and equipment required for continuing to manufacture byre cleaners, passage scrapers and cow brushes and, of course, sought new premises, as John Pollock had decided to sell the factory. This was a major headache as we had all the plant and equipment but no site to move to. John Pollock suggested that we could rent the implement works for a maximum time of two years. However, George Pollock was positive we had to make a clean break away from our historic base.

From apprentice to sales man and now with the potential to be business owner, I eagerly contacted East Ayrshire Council and they offered us premises in Auchinleck, Kilmarnock and Mauchline, but they were either too small, in need of major repair or did not have three-phase power. Within two weeks, I noticed an advert in the *Cumnock Chronicle* for industrial units in Lugar, on the site of the NCB Workshops. I immediately contacted George Pollock who agreed to meet me the next day, discussed with the landlord what was on offer, put our requirements in writing and we could decide soon. The landlord reacted very quickly and we now had premises and were ready to roll. In the meantime, the workforce knew something was happening in the background but were not quite sure what.

On the way home from a job in Aberdeen, I confided in Reid Armour and told him exactly what was happening, including my need to have him on board as a key worker. Reid fully understood the implications and while he was unhappy at not being included in the takeover, he was pleased the company would survive.

In mid-April, a decision was made to go public on the impending changes. We informed the *Scottish Farmer* and an advert was placed with them notifying the change of ownership. Much was still to be sorted out regarding the Tupe Regulations, removal and re-installation of plant and equipment, and transfer of vehicles, etc.

The transfer date was sent and it was decided that I would take over on 1 June 1998, and we could continue at the implement works short term until we had everything sorted out such as gas, electricity and water. By August 1998, we were settled in our new factory, installing a new spray booth, floors painted and 8,600 square feet of manufacturing space. After about four weeks, I was sure I had made a mistake as the building we rented was 16,000 square feet with a wall built, primarily, because I could not afford the rent on the full building.

We continued to operate from a small machine shop/workshop and within a couple of weeks, we secured yet another major job for C. W. S. Agriculture, this time much nearer home at Parkhead farm (Blairgowrie). This unit comprised of five drive units, ten scraper blades, a huge amount of chain and control panels. Other major jobs came our way with three unit systems at Swaffham in Norfolk and Lee Valley Farms in Essex. Lee Valley is better known as the venue for the 2012 Olympic Kayak Events, but it also has a working dairy farm attached. Things were going very well and I was driving approximately 50,000 miles in search of new installations, leaving the workshop in the capable hands of my brother Gerry, who came back to Pollocks on 1 June 1998, having being made redundant in the 1980 cull.

It was important that the business remained consistent to keep stability and customer confidence and we continued to exhibit at the Royal Highland and Ayr shows in 1998 and

6.02 Model of a Rope Scraper System.

beyond. Also, showing in England at the Royal Show, the Great Yorkshire Show and the European Dairy Event.

Gerry coming back into the business was a major step for us as he had plenty of new ideas, one being the rope scraper system. We had looked at rope scrapers some years earlier, and in fact Gerry had built a small scale proto-type which I showed to John Pollock. He commented that it was a clever idea, but I could spend my own money doing the research and development if I so wished. John was a regular visitor to the factory during his retirement and I would bounce ideas off him to gauge his reaction and seek his advice especially on engineering matters. Unfortunately, John was never too see the results of our research and development in rope scrapers as he died suddenly on 22 April 1999, having retired only ten months earlier. This was a devastating blow to the Pollock family and myself, the apparent cause of his death was pneumonia brought on by a chest infection.

John Pollock had many connections and made many friends and acquaintances throughout his working life, none more so than T. R. L. Fraser (Ronnie), who had the sad task of writing his lifelong friend's obituary in *The Herald*. He wrote of John's early days at Mauchline Public School, Gresham House School, and Sedbergh in the Lake District. Also of John being the former captain of Barassie Golf Club, and he noted that John was also secretary of Mauchline Curling Club and an active member of Cumnock Rotary Club, in which he held all major offices.

Ronnie Fraser was a regular visitor to our Highland Show stand and I met him on many occasions. He was a former editor of *Farming News*, a lecturer in Agricultural Economics at Durham and agricultural researcher on the staff of the U.S Embassy in London and later with the BBC as an agricultural correspondent. It was fitting that a journalist with such a high profile should prepare John Pollock's obituary.

6.03 Rope Scraper System prototype in the factory.

6.04 Rope Scraper Systems in production.

Part of the Councils commitment to the new business was to protect their investment by introducing a Business Development Mentor or 'Tormenter' to us. This involved monthly meetings held at our works to develop new ideas and strategies with Terry Houston, a genial Northern Irish Gentleman.

Terry also had access to every Government initiative and grant scheme available. Terry thought that grant aid would be available for this project. He set about gathering all the information and did market research putting a plan together and within a few weeks, we received approval to start work on building a full size working system.

Terry, was a very successful business man and right away he spotted the company's main weakness. The lack of a field representative in England and Wales would be far more detrimental to the business than any other reason. I was very reluctant to start a salesman so early in our history, however in May 1999, we decided to employ a salesman to cover the Midlands, South Wales and the 'Dairy Counties' in the South West of England. Mick Mayer was recommended to us by R. T. C., our Cheshire/Shropshire/North Wales agents, who had previously known Mick from his days with the Hanley Foundry Co and most recently with our competitor in Lancashire (Malgar), which had a habit of going bust.

We appointed Mick Mayer mainly because he required little in-house training. He was set to work right away and retired in 2007, having had a very successful time selling Pollock machines. Since taking over in June 1998, our first task was to stabilise the business, work to our new business plan, increase turnover and grow the work force all within the first two years.

With the test rig built, we now had to look for a site nearby to test our prototype. W. Raphael of Meikle Auchengibbert farm had installed two sets of chain scrapers some years

**POLLOCK**
*farm equipment*

The Directors of Pollock Farm Equipment Ltd
cordially invite you to the official opening of their new premises
by
*Brian Wilson MP*
*Minister of State for Trade and Industry.*

17 September 1998 at 10.45am
Unit 1, IMEX Business Centre, Lugar, Cumnock KA18 3NJ

*R.S.V.P.*
Effie McGhee
Telephone (01290) 427000 Fax (01290) 427013

6.05 Invitation to opening of new works at Lugar, 1998

6.06 Jimmy McGhee talking to Brian Wilson,
Minister for Trade and Industry at Lugar, 1998.

6.07 Jimmy McGhee and Brian Wilson.

earlier from a competitor and was now experiencing problems. We proposed removing one system to yield plenty of spares and substitute it for our own rope scraper system to test in a working environment. Being near the works enabled us to monitor this system very closely, but it worked very well and required little attention.

Terry Houston was very impressed with the operation of this machine and advised us to enter the New Machine category at the Highland Show in 2000. We duly filled in the forms with details of installation sites and waited and much to my delight, on 1 June 2000, we received news that we had been awarded a Silver Medal. This date is significate in as much as it was two years to the day since we took over the company from John Pollock.

Terry Houston's next move was to enter the John Logie Baird Award for Innovation which pitched us alongside hi-tech companies including bio-science, computer, computer science, and genetic companies all seeking awards. We were judged and came out Winners in the Company Category, Ayrshire Regional Awards. We moved on to the finals in Glasgow but no further progress was made.

6.08 Rope scraper installed at Orchardton farm, Cumnock, 2000.

However, with the Regional Winners, we were presented with a prize of £1,000. Rope scrapers were selling very well with around thirty units sold in the first two seasons. Some worked well, others not so well, where the farmers were technically minded. Some expected the rope scraper to work with no maintenance and this was certainly not the case. On one hand, we had a very successful chain scraper which required little attention and a rope scraper which needed the rope kept tight. We sold rope scrapers for a few years along with chain scrapers. Our prototype is still working daily along with quite a few rope systems some nineteen years later.

6.09 Jimmy McGhee, John Spooner, Jimmy Boyd (Provost of East Ayrshire), Gerry McGhee and Fiona Lees, 2000.

Determined to make a success of the business, in January 2000 my wife Effie, joined us at the factory, previously having being employed with Lloyd the Chemist in Auchinleck. Effie, being new to computer work, was sent on a Sage training course, along with Karen the office junior. Both completed the course successfully and on receipt of SAGE certification, Karen immediately applied for a job which required SAGE certification and was successful in her pursuit of a new job. We were back to square one with Effie running the office on her own.

At the turn of the new Millennium, our landlords changed from Imex to Martin J. Mellet, a Northern Ireland Entrepreneur who bought the complex at Lugar.

Within a year, he was offering various parts for sale. He approached me and offered me the whole site for a figure north of £200k. Having only started in June 1998, we thought it was impossible. However, we were making large investments in plant and equipment and at that time, the banks were always looking for more business.

We mulled over Martin Mellet's proposals and made an offer for the 5,600 square feet we occupied plus the remaining 11,000 square feet in the building. After some time and a lot of negotiation, we eventually struck a deal. We had purchased 16,000 square feet of manufacturing space, car parking, and a yard to the rear of the premises - all within three years of our takeover of the business.

Initially, we signed a lease for ten years, paying £850 per month rent with all repairs and maintenance being our responsibilities. Therefore, purchasing the property for £45,000 certainly made sense. We continued to rent the office and the toilet facilities in the main building until August 2003 when we purchased the former NCB Laboratory offices for conversion to a retail shop and offices on the ground floor, with the panel building on the first floor. The conversion cost added to the purchase price meant a total of £15,600 expenditure financed by company profits.

The business was growing fast and we invested in an N. C. controlled saw costing £8,600. This could be programmed and automatically measures, cuts and clamps steel being cut.

Next on our list was to automate the production of rivets for chain making, our usage was phenomenal with ten rivets per metre of chain and at the height of byre cleaner and passage scraper production, we were making approximately 5,000 metres of chain. Purely by chance, my elder brother, Edward, noticed a bankruptcy sale advertised in The Herald for around thirty automatic lathes. Both Gerry and I went to Newhouse Industrial Estate to view the lathes, never having seen such a machine before. Gerry went back a few days later, spoke to the machine setter/operator, who by this time was in the process of being made redundant. He identified the machine most suitable for our jobs, marked it on his list, bid and purchased the machine for £1,250. Along with this lathe came the setter/operator who trained Gerry on the various settings and operation of this 8½ ton beast.

6.10 Highland Show stand 2002.

6.11 Pollock Bale Handlers at the Highland Show 2006.

Paris Show is long remembered as a show to look forward to, however, the 2001 show will be long remembered for the wrong reasons. As we boarded the plane for our return to Prestwick, I heard about an outbreak of Foot and Mouth disease in Cumbria. This outbreak quickly spread and we were restricted in which farms and districts we could work in. Cumbria was by far the worst county hit by foot and mouth, with 843 cases, but it was also prevalent in the South West of Scotland, particularly Dumfriesshire, which happened to be by far our best area for sales. By October 2001, the outbreak was contained, although restrictions on the movement of cattle, sheep and pigs was not relaxed until January 2002. In the short term, we gained a substantial amount of work from this outbreak. However, the damage to the dairy industry became apparent with the number of dairy farmers leaving the industry for good, never to return.

As is the normal situation in agriculture, nothing lasts and systems change. The Co-op announced in late 2001 that their whole agricultural policy was changing and they were closing their whole dairy operations and converting to arable farming.

This was a devastating blow, our largest single customer with machines now reaching their teenage years were all to be obsolete. This decision was universal, the Co-op's dairy farms from Aberdeen to Hampshire in the south were all being closed in a structured exit from dairying.

The last units installed for the Co-op was at a dairy unit built at Blairgowrie (Perthshire), logged as machine numbers 1700-1704. It must be noted that the Co-op were the largest dairy farmers in the UK managing quite a few dairy units on behalf of clients as well as their own estate portfolio.

Just after the foot and mouth disease had been cleared up, Jim Forbes, who manufactured the printed circuit boards, decided to retire. To maintain supplies of the circuit boards, we purchased the entire stock Jim Forbes had made. He also offered us the design and supplier details for us to manufacture in house for a consideration of £20,000.

We considered what options we had and passed the details to our mentor, Terry Houston, to seek some assistance and solve this problem. Terry immediately contacted East Ayrshire Council who very quickly put us in touch with an Innovations Councillor, who came to the factory, discussed what we wanted and after some consultation, he grasped our requirements. On returning to the council headquarters, he drafted up his report. His report was concise and to the point: instead of Printed Circuit Controllers (PCC), we should design a new type of controller using a Programmable Logic Controller (PLC) and load a computer programme via a computer interface. This technology in 2001 was cutting edge and completely over my head as I had problems with mobile phones never mind computers!

Reid Armour was much more confident and set about building a controller, fitted a PLC, wired it up and we then contacted the PLC manufacturer who was very interested to help us. Their technical sales manager, Aldo Pezzani, came to the factory to see our prototype. After one week, he returned to the factory with a computer programme and interface leads, loaded the programme and we were now ready for an onsite test. We installed this unit at Darnlaw farm, Auchinleck where Bryce Sloan looks after his 'Townlaw' herd of Holsteins and waited for any problems or glitches which may occur. We are still waiting today some sixteen years later. One thing which greatly amused me was Aldo's reluctance to go amongst the cows, citing their teeth and the fact that they may bite him – ah townies!

In 2002, Alison Scott, our daughter, joined the company as a clerical assistant. Alison was much more used to computers, and soon she was doing the accounts, management reports and all quotations and letters. With the purchase of the NCB Laboratory in August 2003, we applied for planning permission to convert the lab into a suite of offices with a retail shop. In October 2005, the retail shop opened, stocking wheelbarrows, protective clothing, electric fencing, nuts and bolts and a large selection of household products.

The shop had no existing customers and started off very slowly, taking around £200 in the first week. However, we could continue as no additional staff was required. The retail shop continued to flourish, so much so that we now have two-part time girls in the shop doing some business administration as well as serving customers. The shop today turns over around £2,000 per week consistently throughout the year and really helps the business cash flow.

In 2003, the Co-operative Wholesale Society had decided to give up their dairies. Met the opportunity, we purchased most of the C. W. S. machines back and we proceeded to re-furbish them and sold the machines to customers who could not afford new systems. In March 2003, my wife Effie and I headed to Paris Show. At the Paris Nord Exhibition Centre, I saw a rotary cow brush on display. I enquired about this brush which was Italian made and very well built.

6.12 Rotary Cow Brush

The following week after Paris, we were invited to Italy to see the manufacturing set up of a Agricow. We ordered six brushes and now had a very good brush to offer with our own manufactured brush. To date we have sold around £500k of Italian brushes.

At the end of 2004, we were approached by Davy Laird of Carbello farm to see if we could cure the many problems he was having with a particularly well-designed bale hander for the large rectangular and round bales that he made. One problem we discovered was that the legs of his bale handler were flimsy, made of 4mm box section, the padders were small in comparison to the size of bale and the hydraulic system was exposed.

We set about designing larger paddles and a much stronger box section and a cylinder cover. Our first attempt was tried out at G. McKerrow, Roadinghead farm (Cumnock). It was successful, but still required some tweaking to make it marketable. We addressed the points Davy was concerned about and soon had a marketable unit.

A decision was reached that we should try a pre-production run of five machines, two for Davy Laird, and three for Davy's many silage customers in 2005. With the success of these five units, we decided to double up and make ten units, going on to manufacture twenty-five units so far (2016). Bale handlers will never make a fortune, however, along with rotary cow brushes, they limited the time between passage scraper and byre cleaner production to a minimum.

Next on our agenda was a hydraulic scraper system. The scrapers we were producing had one Achilles heel, they worked very well in regular two or four passages, however, when faced with a single passage or three passages, we were well out on price and losing several sales. In 2004, we started development of our own hydraulic scraper and by the year end, we had a site near Mauchline to test out a prototype - Messrs Caldwell of Ladyyard providing us with the test bed. We proceeded with much more care than with the rope scraper, taking a long time to see if there were any underlying problems and fix them before committing to a production run. This proved to be the correct decision and after a year delay, we decided to offer hydraulic scrapers.

We have been fairly successful and have installed fifty plus units and have completely re-designed the ram box, added a sole plate for the track to run on, reducing wear and generally tided up the units.

In 2004, we installed the last two of eight units for Nanhoron Estate (Pwhelli). This unit saw the completion of a project for 180 cows double to 360 cows and finally doubled

161

again to 720 cows. Many orders were still coming in but the family farms we relied on for the bulk of our work were being squeezed on every front by rising feed costs, coupled with a low milk price. One family bucking the trend were T. & C. Hall of Woolrow farm (Shelley, near Huddersfield).

Working long hours took its toll and in 2005, I suffered a Transient Ischaemic Attack (stroke) which was to prove extremely debilitating. Following an absence from work and some sixteen weeks at speech therapy, I returned to the helm and threw myself straight back into work.

2005 had proved to be a difficult year, health wise, but every cloud has a silver lining. I was travelling to speech therapy on 18 July and before we had arrived, my wife had noticed that I was wearing two different socks. Almost immediately thereafter, we received a call to say that our new granddaughter had been born. Effie, ever the snappy dresser, refused to allow me to visit the hospital with my odd socks and quickly arranged a visit to Poundstretcher for a new pair. Our granddaughter, Iona, was born a healthy 7lb 13oz and both mother and daughter were doing well.

By the end of 2006, we had installed our 2000th unit with machines Numbers 2000-2006 being installed at Woolrow. This investment included a new milk parlour, cubicle and feed units with floor grooved to accept our chain complete with delta wing blades.

At the Royal Highland Show in 2006, we exhibited or new bale handling system which was very well received.

Another family farm that was investing heavily in the future was John Harries of Vellinidre (Goodwick, near Fishguard). We had previously sold him four scraper systems and we were now building a new diary unit requiring a further two systems. At the same time, Wales was buzzing with new dairies from Pembroke in the South to Pwhelli in the north and Pollock Farm Equipment was chosen for quite

162

a few of these units. We installed five units for Tom Phillips & Son at Ty-Mawr farm. Tom will be known to many Holstein breeders as both judge, exhibitor and generally as a very capable farmer.

6.13 Jimmy McGhee with the Unisys John Logie Baird Award, 2000.

They say that all good things come to those who wait and in 2005, we priced up a job for H. Neilson of Park farm (East Kilbride), but unfortunately, we lost out to De Boer Systems. However, in 2009, after a series of breakdowns, Mr Neilson came back to us and we installed a further four units for him. Throughout the 2000s, we increased our turnover from a low point in 1998 of £400k per annum to £700k in 2010 and increased year on year, even although farmers were feeling the pinch, with low milk prices and the well-documented banking crisis.

6.14 A restored Pollock's Ideal Potato Digger.

6.15 A restored Pollock's cart, modified with pneumatic wheels and drawbar.

Towards the end of 2008, we were asked to price a system with a difference for J. Jamieson and Son, Woodhead (Annan). John Jamieson wanted a system which scraped both passages at the same time instead of scraping one top to bottom, reversing and scraping the second passage. His idea was to scrape the passages with a fix scraper discharging to a slurry channel at either end of the shed and one in the middle. We redesigned the scraper blade and discussed the control system with Reid, who altered the standard PLC programme and we then had a single scraping system.

The implications of a single scraper were huge. A normal scraper in a shed, 150 feet long, took approximately thirty minutes to scrape the shed, whereas our single scraping machine could do the job in fifteen minutes. The customer then had the option to scrape every two hours with a running time of fifteen minutes or three hours a day instead of six hours, saving on running costs and wear and tear on the system. We took this a stage further and designed a 'Gull Wing Blade' which allowed the customer to scrape a floor which was tapered from the cubicles to the centre of the passage to a groove for the chain. The theory behind this was the urine for the cows would drain into the chain channel and leave only the solids to scrape.

In the years 2010-11, farm incomes recovered with farmers who had contracts with large supermarkets like Tesco, Sainsbury, and the Co-op, or Cadbury's and Nestle who were also large buyers of milk. However, some smaller producers were still on breadline contracts with the smaller milk buyers. Throughout 2012-13, there was a mass exodus from the dairy industry and we were now facing the least number of milk producers in the whole of the UK.

Turnover increased to a high of £850k in 2014. Now in 2015, the general economic climate for farming in the UK is depressed and dairying will never be the same again.

In August 2015, whilst out on my normal sales visits to Dumfries, to see Hugh McClymont of the Crichton Royal farms, I took ill on route. I immediately phoned my wife to say I was ill, she in turn telephoned Calum McDermid who for some time had been supplying us with our nut and bolt requirements. Being only three quarters a mile away, Calum attended right away. On seeing me, Calum phoned 999 and within two minutes, an ambulance arrived and took me to hospital. I ended up at the Royal. However, it was the Dumfries Royal Infirmary where after a four-day stay in hospital, I was allowed home.

This was a wake-up call for me, and after being discharged from Dumfries, I was referred to the Cardiac Specialist in Ayr. It transpired that I had suffered a heart attack and damaged my heart. The outcome of all these tests showed that I required a triple bypass and new aortic valve.

On 21 February 2016, I was admitted to the Golden Jubilee Hospital in Clydebank to undergo the surgery I required to bring me back to good health. After the surgery, I took pneumonia which set me back a few weeks but gradually got stronger. After nineteen days in the Golden Jubilee Hospital I was fit to go home.

Ayr Show in 2016 was out of the question, but I had my sights set on the Royal Highland Show. I knew within myself that I was never going to be fit enough to continue as before so I appointed William Robertson, who had served his apprenticeship with us, to the position of Sales Engineer. William managed to do all the sales visits, along with servicing our existing machines and gaining sales knowledge along the way.

I am immensely proud of where we have come in the business. At present, we have fourteen employees – two of whom are part time and the remaining twelve full time. Since the transfer of business in 1998, we have never made anyone

6.16 Restored Turnip Slicers

6.17 Restored Curd Mill

6.18 Restored Food Cooler

6.19 Hydraulic Scraper

redundant and always tried to keep our staff busy by working overtime in periods when our order book was healthy.

Looking at our employees today, of the fourteen, five of those have been with the company now for over twenty years, namely my brother Gerry McGhee, John Gibson Snr, Norman Anderson, Reid Armour and myself.

Regarding staff with over ten years' employment, we have Ian Barbour, Willie Robertson, and my daughter, Alison Scott. Finally, less than ten years with the company we have Craig Wilson, Tony Clark, Billy Clelland, Liz Hodge, Johanna Nicoll and our Saturday girl, Chelsea Aitken.

The time our employees have spent within the business plays testament to the hard work the Pollock family put into the business and the work that has continued under my regime.

Personally, I will have completed fifty years with the business, through its various names - A. & W. Pollock, John Pollock, and for the last eighteen years trading as Pollock Farm Equipment Ltd. I will have joined an illustrious line-up of people who have served fifty years or more with Pollocks in its century and a half.

Having the opportunity to work in the business and to promote the many farm equipment implements has been inspiring and has shaped the way I have done business over the years. The Pollock family in its various business forms and the company as it stands now have played a part in many shows, including the Ayr Show since 1873, the Highland Show since 1875, and the Royal Agricultural Show at Derby, from 1885 until the show closed. We also exhibited for many years at Belfast from 1895 in conjunction with T. & J. McErvel. Indeed, s far as the Royal Highland Show is concerned, we have held the same stand since 1960.

It has been an honour and privilege to work my way up through the ranks with the Pollock family and be part of this illustrious firm now known as Pollock Farm Equipment Ltd.

It has been a great source of comfort and enjoyment researching this book and looking at all archives, articles and pictures.

6.20 Jimmy McGhee with Princess Anne at Ayr Show, 2003.

# Appendix I : Patents

A.D. 1878, *5th July.* N° 2685.

## Machine for Topping and Tailing Turnips and Digging Potatoes.

---

*(This Invention received Provisional Protection only.)*

PROVISIONAL SPECIFICATION left by Andrew Pollock at the Office of the Commissioners of Patents on the 5th July 1878.

ANDREW POLLOCK, of Mauchline, in the County of Ayr, North Britain. "A NEW OR IMPROVED MACHINE FOR TOPPING AND TAILING TURNIPS OR OTHER
5 ANALOGOUS ROOT CROPS, THE SAME BEING ALSO APPLICABLE FOR REMOVING POTATOES FROM THE GROUND."

This Invention relates to improvements in that class of machine at present in use for digging potatoes, wherein the digging or potato removing instrument consists of a series of arms carrying forks or prongs at their extremities arranged radially, so
10 that when revolving at right angles to the direction in which the machine is drawn the prongs or forks successively knock or lift the potatoes from out of the ground.

Under the present improvements by which the machine is adapted for cutting off the tops and removing the tails from turnips and other root crops of an analogous
15 kind, the revolving arms in place of being formed with prongs or forks are fitted with knives, which as they revolve cut off the tops of the turnips.

The knives are also capable of being lifted or lowered according to the height above ground of the roots from off which the tops have to be cut.

The after or rear part of the machine is furnished with a combined lifting and
20 tail-cutting instrument of an angular shape, and which is formed with cutting edges.

When the machine is being drawn over the ground this instrument passes under the turnip or analogous root at a depth sufficient for the cutting edges to catch upon the upper or thick part of the tail and cut it through. The body of the

*Pollock's Improved Machine for Topping and Tailing Turnips, &c.*

turnip or analogous root being thus removed from the tail, lies loose on the ground ready for being picked up.

 It is to be understood that by removing the arms with the knives and the rear cutting instrument, and placing the ordinary arms with prongs upon the revolving shaft, the said machine may be used for lifting potatoes or other roots, wherein 5 topping and tailing operations are unnecessary.

LONDON: Printed by GEORGE EDWARD EYRE and WILLIAM SPOTTISWOODE,<br>Printers to the Queen's most Excellent Majesty.<br>For Her Majesty's Stationery Office.<br>1879.

1878 Patent - Page 2

## PROVISIONAL SPECIFICATION.

## Improvements in Potato Digging Machines.

I, ANDREW POLLOCK of Mauchline in the County of Ayr, Agricultural Implement and machine maker, do hereby declare the nature of the said invention for " IMPROVEMENTS IN POTATO DIGGING MACHINES " to be as follows :—

This invention which has for its object improvements in potato digging machines
5 relates to the apparatus by which the "graipes" are thrown into and out of action.

The apparatus as improved consists of a crank arm secured to or formed on the usual hand lever employed in lowering and raising the rear end of the frame, carrying the "sock" and the "graipes," into and out of working position.
10 This hand lever is situated on a shaft or stud at the front end of the frame and the crank arm on it is connected by a rod or link either direct to the clutch by which the usual bevel pinion on the shaft carrying the "graipes" is thrown into and out of gear with the bevel wheel on the main axle of the machine, or an intermediate lever may be used between the link and the clutch. By means of
15 the invention the same action which lowers and raises the "graipes" into and out of working position also gears and disengages them with the bevel wheel on the main axle.

Dated this Thirtieth day of April 1885.

GEO. M. CRUIKSHANK, Fel. Inst. P.A.,
20 Agent.

COMPLETE SPECIFICATION.

## Improvements in Potato Digging Machines.

I, ANDREW POLLOCK of Mauchline in the County of Ayr, Agricultural Implement and Machine Maker, do hereby declare the nature of this invention and in what manner the same is to be performed, to be particularly described and ascertained in and by the following statement :—

This invention which has for its object improvements in potato digging machines 5 relates to the apparatus by which the " graipes " are thrown into and out of action and as seen in elevation at fig. 1 and in plan at fig. 2, of the annexed drawings the apparatus as improved consists of a crank arm A, one end of which is centred on a pin fixed in a bracket B, whilst its other end is acted on by the usual hand lever C, employed in lowering and raising the rear end of the frame D, carrying the 10 " sock " and the " graipes " into and out of working position. The hand lever C, is centred upon the axle of the front wheel E of the digging machine and it is connected to the frame D, by a pin or stud F, bolted or otherwise secured to the front of the said frame the bracket B, carrying the crank arm A being also situated upon the said pin or stud. As shown by the drawings the arm A, is connected by 15 a rod or link G to one end of a lever H which is centred on the frame D, and whose other end acts on a clutch I, situated on the shaft J, carrying the graipes so as to render the bevel pinion K loose upon the said shaft and stop the rotation of the graipes when desired.

It will thus be seen that by means of the invention the same action which 20 lowers and raises the graipes into and out of working position also gears and disengages them with the bevel wheel L on the main axle M of the machine for, when the hand lever C, is depressed in the direction of the arrow fig. 1, the said movement depresses the forward end of the frame D, which turning on the axle M as a centre causes the graipes carried by the rear end of the frame to be elevated. 25 The lever C, on being depressed also comes in contact with the crank arm A, which moving in the direction of the arrow fig. 1, draws the link G, forward, and the said link acting on the lever H throws the clutch out of gear with the pinion K whereby the said pinion is rendered loose upon the shaft J and the rotation of the said shaft with its graipes is stopped. When the hand lever C, is again elevated 30 so as to lower the graipes and sock into working position the spring N on the shaft J, forces the clutch I back into gear with the pinion K thereby rotating the shaft J, and with it the graipes.

The hand lever C, is retained in the position to which it is adjusted by means of a spring lever and rack quadrant as is well understood in practice in such 35 machines.

1885 Patent - Page 2

*Pollock's Improvements in Potato Digging Machines.*

Having now particularly described and ascertained the nature of my said invention and in what manner the same is to be performed I declare that what I claim is

In a potato digging machine the combination of the crank arm A, link G, 5 lever H, clutch I and spring N whereby on actuating the hand lever C, the lowering of the graipes into working position and gearing them with the driving axle or the raising of the graipes out of working position and disengaging them with the driving axle are performed simultaneously substantially as described.

Dated this Twenty-ninth day of January 1886.

10
CRUIKSHANK & FAIRWEATHER,
Agents.

LONDON: Printed by EYRE AND SPOTTISWOODE,
Printers to the Queen's most Excellent Majesty.
For Her Majesty's Stationery Office.

1886.

1885 Patent - Page 3

A.D. 1885. MAY 1. N° 5396.
POLLOCK'S COMPLETE SPECIFICATION.

(1 SHEET)

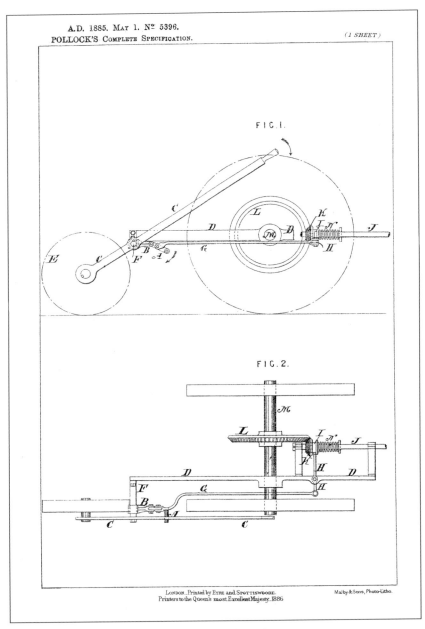

FIG. 1.

FIG. 2.

LONDON. Printed by EYRE and SPOTTISWOODE.
Printers to the Queen's most Excellent Majesty. 1886.

Malby & Sons, Photo-Litho.

1885 Patent - Page 4

# N° 20,412

# A.D. 1889

Date of Application, 19th Dec., 1889
Complete Specification Left, 16th Sept., 1890—Accepted, 18th Oct., 1890

## PROVISIONAL SPECIFICATION.

### Improvements in Hay Bogies, Sledges, or Carriers.

I, ANDREW POLLOCK of Mauchline in the County of Ayr, Agricultural Engineer, do hereby declare the nature of this invention to be as follows :—

This invention, which has for its object improvements in bogies, sledges, or carriers for transporting hay or other cut crops from the field to the stack yard or elsewhere,
5 relates to an improved disposition of the roller or barrel arranged at the front end of the platform of such carriers and whereon the binding or holding chains or ropes are wound. Under the invention the said barrel, which is provided with pawl and ratchet gear for turning it, instead of projecting above the front end of the platform, is so arranged as to have the highest part of its circumference level with
10 or below the upper side of the platform whereby, when it is desired, the material can be delivered or drawn over the front end of the platform more easily, and a longer platform can also be obtained.

Dated this Eighteenth day of December 1889.

CRUIKSHANK & FAIRWEATHER,
15          62, Saint Vincent Street, Glasgow, Agents.

## COMPLETE SPECIFICATION.

### Improvements in Hay Bogies, Sledges, or Carriers.

I, ANDREW POLLOCK of Mauchline in the County of Ayr, Agricultural Engineer, do hereby declare the nature of this invention and in what manner the same is to be
20 performed, to be particularly described and ascertained in and by the following statement :—

This invention which has for its object improvements in bogies sledges or carriers for transporting hay or other cut crops from the field to the stack yard or elsewhere relates to an improved disposition of the roller or barrel arranged at the front end
25 of the platform of such carriers and whereon the binding or holding chains or ropes are wound.

As shewn by Figure 1 of the annexed drawings, which is a view of the improved carrier in travelling position and by Figure 2, where the apparatus is in position to receive its load, the said barrel a, which is provided with pawl and ratchet gear b,
30 for turning it instead of projecting above the front end of the platform c, is so arranged as to have the highest part of its circumference level with or below the upper side of the platform whereby when it is desired the load can be delivered or drawn over the front end of the platform more easily, and a longer platform can also be obtained.

35 Having now particularly described and ascertained the nature of the said invention and in what manner the same is to be performed I declare that what I claim is :—

In apparatus of the class set forth arranging the roller or barrel a, substantially as and for the purpose described with reference to the drawings annexed.

40    Dated this Fifteenth day of September 1890.

CRUIKSHANK & FAIRWEATHER,
         62, Saint Vincent Street, Glasgow, Agents.

London : Printed for Her Majesty's Stationery Office, by Darling & Son, Ltd.—1890.

1889 Patent - Page 1

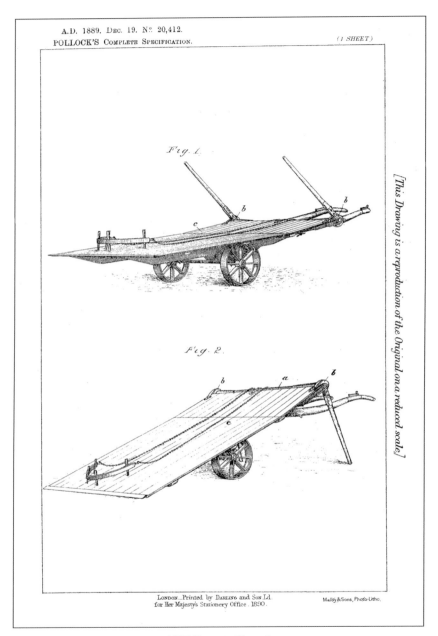

Fig. 1.

Fig. 2.

[This Drawing is a reproduction of the Original on a reduced scale.]

London...Printed by Darling and Son Ld.
for Her Majesty's Stationery Office . 1890 .

Malby & Sons, Photo-Litho.

1889 Patent - Page 2

178

N° 1880

A.D. 1894

Date of Application, 29th Jan., 1894
Complete Specification Left, 24th Oct., 1894—Accepted, 24th Nov., 1894

## PROVISIONAL SPECIFICATION.

### A Combined Land Roller and Broad-cast Seed Sower.

I, ANDREW POLLOCK, of Mauchline, in the County of Ayr, North Britain, Agricultural Implement Maker, do hereby declare the nature of this invention to be as follows :—

This invention relates to a combined land roller and broad cast sower. The
5 invention consists in an ordinary land roller having the driving shaft extending beyond the roller frame. To the end of the driving shaft there is geared a cog wheel or pulley carrying a chain on to another smaller chain or pulley geared to the end of the shaft which passes through the sower and which keeps the seed therein in constant agitation so long as the roller is in motion. The sower is placed
10 on the upper side of roller and is so arranged that the seed can either fall in front of it and so break the stream, or the ground can first be rolled and the seed fall from the sower at the back or hinder end of the roller.

Dated this 27th day of January 1894.

BOTTOMLEY & LIDDLE,
15 154, St. Vincent Street, Glasgow, Applicant's Agents.


## COMPLETE SPECIFICATION.

### A Combined Land Roller and Broad-cast Seed Sower.

I, ANDREW POLLOCK, of Mauchline, in the County of Ayr, North Britain, Agricultural Implement Maker, do hereby declare the nature of this invention
20 and in what manner the same is to be performed to be particularly described and ascertained in and by the following statement :—

My invention relates to a combined land roller and broad cast seed sower.

In order that my invention may be properly understood and readily carried into effect I will describe the same, reference being made to the accompanying drawing
25 of the machine constructed according to my improvements.

The invention consists of an ordinary land roller A having the driving shaft B extending beyond the roller frame. To the end of the driving shaft B there is geared a cog wheel C or pulley carrying a chain D on to another smaller wheel E or pulley geared to the end of the shaft F which passes through an ordinary seed
30 sower G and which keeps the seed therein in constant agitation so long as the roller is in motion. The sower G is placed on the upper side of roller A and the seed falls in front of it, which breaks the stream and scatters the seed more evenly on the land, or the ground can first be rolled and by turning the seed sower G round the reverse way the seed fall from it at the back of the roller, and the stream
35 is broken in a similar manner.

I may fix an apron at bottom of seed box to prevent the seed from being blown away by the wind.

*Pollock's Combined Land Roller and Broad-cast Seed Sower.*

Having now particularly described and ascertained the nature of my said invention and in what manner the same is to be performed I declare that what I claim is :—

The combined land roller and broad cast seed sower constructed and operating in the manner substantially as described and shown on the accompanying drawing.    5

Dated this 22nd day of October 1894.

BOTTOMLEY & LIDDLE,
154, St. Vincent Street, Glasgow, Applicant's Agents.

London : Printed for Her Majesty's Stationery Office, by Darling & Son, Ltd.—1894

1894 Patent - Page 2

180

A.D. 1894. Jan. 29. Nᵒ. 1880.
POLLOCK'S Complete Specification.

(1 SHEET)

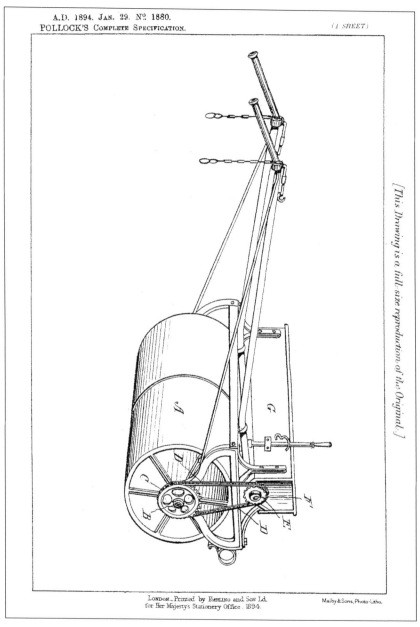

[This Drawing is a full-size reproduction of the Original.]

London.—Printed by Darling and Son Ld.
for Her Majestys Stationery Office. 1894.

Malby & Sons, Photo-Litho.

1894 Patent - Page 3

N.° 18,679  A.D. 1896

Date of Application, 24th Aug., 1896—Accepted, 10th Oct., 1896

COMPLETE SPECIFICATION.

## An Improvement in Machines for Collecting Hay and the like.

I, ANDREW POLLOCK of Mauchline, in the County of Ayr, North Britain, Agricultural Engineer, do hereby declare the nature of this invention and in what manner the same is to be performed to be particularly described and ascertained in and by the following statement :—

5      In existing machines for collecting or gathering hay and the like from the winnows on small coils or rods the teeth are not sufficiently supported and hence they wabble about and are therefore liable to miss some of the hay as the machine is being propelled. The object therefore of my invention is to obviate this which I accomplish by providing stays which are fixed to the teeth and backbone of the

10 machine.

     In order that my invention may be properly understood and readily carried into effect I have appended one sheet of drawings of which

     Figure 1 is a front elevation of a machine shewing my improvements ; and

     Figure 2 a detached view shewing more clearly the shape of the stays and how

15 they are fixed.

     A is the backbone of the machine, and B are the teeth while C are the stays. The stays are of triangular shape with downwardly projecting ends c which lie against the side of the teeth so that they can be bolted, rivetted, or otherwise fixed thereto, while the upper end or angle lies against the backbone and in a

20 similar manner is also connected thereto, all as shewn in the drawings.

     Having now particularly described and ascertained the nature of my said invention and in what manner the same is to be performed I declare that what I claim is :—

     In machines for collecting or gathering hay and the like supporting the teeth

25 by means of stays, substantially as and for the purpose hereinbefore described and illustrated on the accompanying sheet of drawings.

     Dated this 22nd day of August 1896.

BOTTOMLEY & LIDDLE,
154, St. Vincent Street, Glasgow, Applicant's Agents.

London : Printed for Her Majesty's Stationery Office, by Darling & Son, Ltd.—1896

1896 Patent - Page 1

A.D. 1896. Aug. 24. N°. 18,679.
POLLOCK'S Complete Specification.

(1 SHEET)

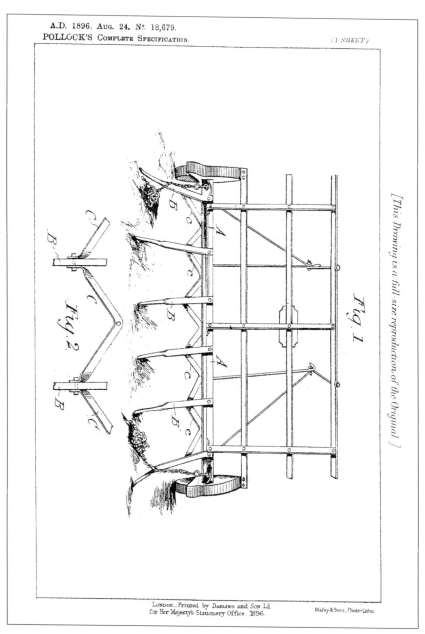

London.. Printed by Darling and Son Ld.
for Her Majesty's Stationery Office . 1896.

Malby & Sons, Photo-Litho.

1896 Patent - Page 2

183

# N° 6877

# A.D. 1900

*Date of Application, 12th Apr., 1900—Accepted, 2nd June, 1900*

COMPLETE SPECIFICATION.

## Improvements in Hay Bogies, Sledges, or Carriers, the same being also Applicable for Carrying Sheep, Calves, or other Light Cattle.

I, ANDREW POLLOCK, Agricultural Engineer, of Mauchline, in the County of Ayr, North Britain, do hereby declare the nature of this invention and in what manner the same is to be performed to be particularly described and ascertained in and by the following statement:—

5   My invention relates to improvements in hay bogies, sledges, or carriers for transporting hay or other cut crops from the field to the stackyard or elsewhere, and is a further development of my prior Patent No. 20412 A.D. 1889, and has reference more particularly to the construction of the barrel on which the ropes or chains are wound and also to the construction of the hub of the wheel. The
10 invention is also applicable for carrying sheep, calves, or other light cattle.

In order that my invention may be properly understood and more readily carried into effect, I have appended one sheet of drawings, of which,

  Figure 1 is a front elevation of the barrel.

  Figure 2 a view of section of the hub with the bush in position.

15   Figure 3 a separate view of the bush referred to.

  Figure 4 is a view of part of the bogie when it is to be used for carrying sheep, calves, or other light cattle.

In carrying out my invention, I make the barrel A of larger diameter than that presently in use and with a cone-shape piece B, and B¹ on each end to prevent
20 the ropes or chains from slipping off. The ends $b$ and $b^1$ of these cone-shaped pieces B and B¹ are of a diameter anything greater than $5\frac{1}{2}''$ and the flanges $b^2$ and $b^3$ greater than $9\frac{1}{2}''$.

The hub C, is constructed with a recess or opening into which a tapered bush D having flanges $d$ is inserted and fixed to the hub by means of bolts $e$, or
25 other suitable manner. The object of constructing the hub in this manner is to be able to repair a wheel by inserting a new bush when the axle bearing becomes worn, in place of having occasion to supply a new wheel altogether.

When the bogie is to be used for carrying sheep, calves, or other light cattle sides G and ends G¹ are bolted or otherwise fixed to the platform, thereby form-
30 ing an enclosure into which the cattle are placed.

Having now particularly described and ascertained the nature of my said invention and in what manner the same is to be performed, I declare that what I claim is:—

  1. In hay bogies, sledges, or carriers, constructing the barrel of larger diameter
35 and with a cone-shaped piece on each end having a diameter, anything greater than $5\frac{1}{2}''$ and with a flange, greater than $9\frac{1}{2}''$, substantially as and for the purposes hereinbefore described and illustrated on the accompanying sheet of drawings.

  2. In hay bogies, sledges, or carriers, constructing the hub or axle of the wheel with a moveable bush, substantially as and for the purposes hereinbefore
40 described and illustrated on the accompanying sheet of drawings.

3. Constructing the bogie so that it can, when required, be utilized for carrying sheep, calves, or other light cattle, substantially as described and illustrated on the accompanying sheet of drawings.

Dated this 11th day of April 1900.

BOTTOMLEY & LIDDLE,      5

154, St. Vincent Street, Glasgow, Applicant's Patent Agents.

Redhill: Printed for Her Majesty's Stationery Office, by Malcomson & Co., Ltd.—1900.

1900 Patent - Page 2

185

A.D. 1900. April 12. N⁰ 6877.
POLLOCK'S Complete Specification.

(1 SHEET)

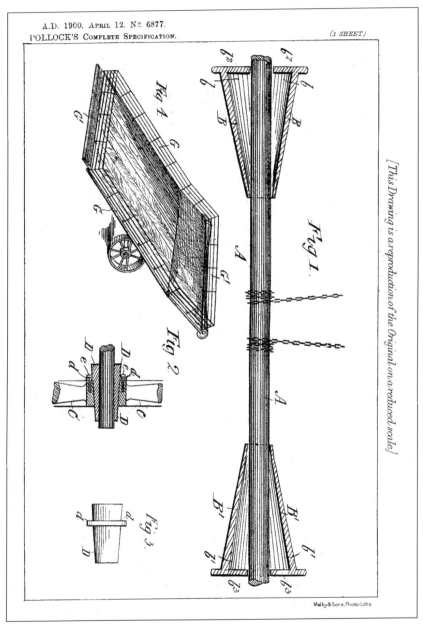

[This Drawing is a reproduction of the Original on a reduced scale.]

Malby & Sons, Photo-Litho.

1900 Patent - Page 3

186

# Appendix II : Catalogues

## A. & W. POLLOCK,
### IMPLEMENT WORKS,
## MAUCHLINE, AYRSHIRE.

## TIPPING OR COUP CART
### FOR FARM OR GENERAL WORK.

|  | TO CARRY. | DEPTH OF SIDES. | SIZE OF TYRES. | PRICE. |
|---|---|---|---|---|
| No. B 2 | 25 Cwts. | 14 ins. | $2\frac{1}{2}'' \times \frac{5}{8}''$ | £29 15 0 |
| ,, B 3 | 27 ,, | 15 ,, | $2\frac{1}{2}'' \times \frac{3}{4}''$ | £30 7 6 |
| ,, B 4 | 30 ,, | 16 ,, | $2\frac{1}{2}'' \times \frac{3}{4}''$ | £31 0 0 |
| ,, B 5 | 30 ,, | 17 ,, | $2\frac{1}{2}'' \times \frac{7}{8}''$ | £31 12 6 |
| ,, B 6 | 35 ,, | 18 ,, | $2\frac{1}{2}'' \times 1''$ | £32 5 0 |

Top Sideboards, 6 ins. deep, included in above prices.
Harvest Frames, - - - - - £3 per Set extra.
Wheels with Tyres 4 ins. broad, - - £2 ~~extra~~ 30/-

The above Carts are fitted with strong Spring Locks, which have
ready facility for tilting and tightening up.

### CARTS WITH COVERS FOR SANITARY AND OTHER PURPOSES
### TO SPECIAL ORDER.

# FAST-BODY CART

### (With Harvest Frames)

#### FOR FARM OR GENERAL WORK.

| | TO CARRY. | DEPTH OF SIDES. | SIZE OF TYRES. | PRICE. | | |
|---|---|---|---|---|---|---|
| No. A 1 | 20 Cwts. | 13 ins. | $2\frac{1}{4}'' \times \frac{5}{8}''$ | £28 | 2 | 6 |
| ,, A 2 | 25 ,, | 14 ,, | $2\frac{1}{2}'' \times \frac{5}{8}''$ | £28 | 15 | 0 |
| ,, A 3 | 27 ,, | 15 ,, | $2\frac{1}{2}'' \times \frac{3}{4}''$ | £29 | 7 | 6 |
| ,, A 4 | 30 ,, | 16 ,, | $2\frac{1}{2}'' \times \frac{3}{4}''$ | £30 | 0 | 0 |
| ,, A 5 | 30 ,, | 17 ,, | $2\frac{1}{2}'' \times \frac{7}{8}''$ | £30 | 12 | 6 |
| ,, A 6 | 35 ,, | 18 ,, | $2\frac{1}{2}'' \times \frac{7}{8}''$ | £31 | 5 | 0 |
| ,, A 7 | 35 ,, | 20 ,, | $2\frac{1}{2}'' \times 1''$ | £32 | 5 | 0 |

Top Sideboards, 6 ins. deep, included in above prices.

Harvest Frames (as illustrated),  -  -  **£3** per Set extra.

Wheels with Tyres 4 ins. broad,  -  -  **£2** extra. *30/-*

---

The Framing and Shafts of all Carts are made of Selected Home-Grown, Well-Seasoned Oaks. Wheels 52″ or 54″ as desired. The Naves are of Best Scotch Elm, Spokes of Oak, and Felloes of Ash.

---

Axles of Best Scrap Iron, laid with Steel, Turned and Case Hardened, and are famed for long wear and easy running.

188

# HARVEST CART.

### AYRSHIRE PATTERN.

The above is Strongly Built and Well Finished.
The Framing is of Oak, Rails of Ash, and Shafts of Best Larch.
Wheels 52″ or 54″ diameter; Tyres $2\frac{1}{2}″ \times \frac{3}{4}″$.

### Price, ~ ~ £26 0s. 0d..

# HAY OR HARVEST CART.

### With Circle Capes over Wheels.

Hay Cart, Strongly Built and Well Finished.
The Framing and Shafts are all made of Oak, and the
Rails of Ash.

### Price, ~ ~ £28 0s. 0d.

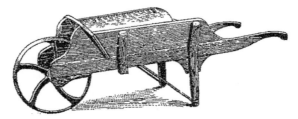
190

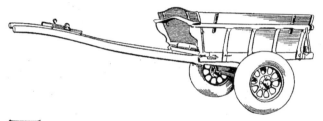

# POLLOCK'S CARTS
## FITTED WITH
## DUNLOP PNEUMATIC LAND TYRES
### AND WITH TOPSIDEBOARDS 7″ DEEP.

|  | FAST BODY. | | COUP BODY. | |
|---|---|---|---|---|
| Cart with Sides 14″ deep. .. | No. A2, | **£29.** | No. B2, | **£30.** |
| Cart with Sides 16″ deep. .. | No. A4, | **£30.** | No. B4, | **£31.** |
| Cart with Sides 18″ deep. .. | No. A6, | **£31.** | No. B6, | **£32.** |

Tyres on above Carts are 8″ diam., and Axles are $2\frac{1}{4}$″ square section.

Nos. A2 and B2 can be supplied with 7″ Tyres
and 2″ square Axles at **£1** less.

Dunlop Land Wheels, fitted with 8″ Tyres,
complete with $2\frac{1}{4}$″ square Axles and Axle
Clips or Axle drilled for Pins, .. .. ..     **£14 5s.** per Set.

Dunlop Land Wheels, fitted with 7″ Tyres,
complete with 2″ square Axle and Axle
Clips or Axle drilled for Pins, .. .. ..     **£13 5s.** per Set.

Harvest Frames to suit Carts, .. .. .. ..     **£3** per Set.

Harvest Ladders to suit Carts,    .. .. ..     **£4** per Set.

Above Carts are all made with Wheel Centres 4′ 8″.

SOLD BY—

POl
farm

# CLEAN, HEALTH

John Pollock (Mauchline) Limited represent the quality and service customers have come to expect from a company which has manufactured farm implements, machinery and equipment for more than 100 years.

Wholly owned and managed by the Pollock family, the company has received numerous medals and awards for original design and construction of implements and machinery.

Today, innovative technology continues to be an integral feature of a design philosophy which has made Pollock one of the largest manufacturers and installers of automated cleaning systems in livestock premises throughout the United Kingdom.

Success in this field has also been reflected in the overseas market. Pollock now export automated cleaning systems and animal welfare equipment to many countries including:

- REPUBLIC OF IRELAND
- CANADA
- UNITED STATES OF AMERICA
- SAUDI ARABIA
- JAPAN

In addition, Pollock systems have been installed in the majority of Scotland's leading agricultural research and educational institutions.

Unlike many farm equipment suppliers, Pollock manufactures almost all its equipment at its own factory in Mauchline, Ayrshire, the heartland of one of the most intensive livestock rearing areas in Europe.

"Superior" class chain and purpose-design motor controllers are just two of the specialised components produced to give Pollock a unique advantage in covering a wide range of intensive livestock housing situations.

*ment*

# , HAPPY COWS!

Although primarily concerned with milking cows, Pollock systems have been installed to meet the requirements of:

- BEEF CATTLE
- PIGS
- SHEEP
- POULTRY
- DUCKS
- RABBITS
- RED DEER

Delivery and installation, either direct or through appointed agents, are key factors in the Pollock customer service which offers an after-sales commitment to maintaining equipment in prime running condition.

All company services are based on a skilled and experienced workforce. All new members of staff undergo established training procedures within the factory and in terms of external customer relations.

The company adopts a fully computerised approach to:

- ACCOUNTING
- CONTROL SYSTEMS
- STOCK CONTROL
- DESIGN

John Pollock (Mauchline) Limited recognise the 1990's as a decade of challenge in terms of environmental conservation, pollution control and animal welfare in farmstead engineering.

Existing and potential customers are assured that Pollock, as leaders in this technology, will build on the success of the past to meet the demands of the future.

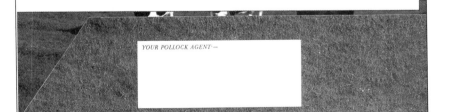

*YOUR POLLOCK AGENT:—*

195